Mathematics:
Dr. Richard Lodholz
Parkway School District
St. Louis, MO

Middle School Specialist:
Daniel Rodriguez
Principal
Pomona, CA

Misconceptions:
Dr. Charles W. Anderson
Michigan State University
East Lansing, MI

Dr. Edward L. Smith
Michigan State University
East Lansing, MI

Multicultural:
Bernard L. Charles
Senior Vice President
Quality Education for Minorities Network
Washington, DC

Paul B. Janeczko
Poet
Hebron, MA

James R. Murphy
Math Teacher
La Guardia High School
New York, NY

Clifford E. Trafzer
Professor and Chair, Ethnic Studies
University of California, Riverside
Riverside, CA

Physical Science:
Gretchen M. Gillis
Geologist
Maxus Exploration Company
Dallas, TX

Henry C. McBay
Professor of Chemistry
Morehouse College and Clark Atlanta University
Atlanta, GA

Wendell H. Potter
Associate Professor of Physics
Department of Physics
University of California, Davis
Davis, CA

Claudia K. Viehland
Educational Consultant, Chemist
Sigma Chemical Company
St. Louis, MO

Reading:
Charles Temple, Ph.D.
Associate Professor of Education
Hobart and William Smith Colleges
Geneva, NY

Safety:
Janice Sutkus
Program Manager: Education
National Safety Council
Chicago, IL

Science Technology and Society (STS):
William C. Kyle, Jr.
Director, School Mathematics and Science Center
Purdue University
West Lafayette, IN

Social Studies:
Jean Craven
District Coordinator of Curriculum Development
Albuquerque Public Schools
Albuquerque, NM

Students Acquiring English:
Mario Ruiz
Pomona, CA

W9-CZK-856

Fog is a colloid.

3

Changes in Matter

Lessons   **Themes**

Macmillan/McGraw-Hill Science

CHANGES IN MATTER

AUTHORS

Mary Atwater
The University of Georgia

Prentice Baptiste
University of Houston

Lucy Daniel
Rutherford County Schools

Jay Hackett
University of Northern Colorado

Richard Moyer
University of Michigan, Dearborn

Carol Takemoto
Los Angeles Unified School District

Nancy Wilson
Sacramento Unified School District

Macmillan/McGraw-Hill School Publishing Company
New York   Chicago   Columbus

Water is matter.

MACMILLAN / McGRAW-HILL

SCIENCE TURNS MINDS ON ™

Derrick R. Lavoie
Assistant Professor of Science Education
Montana State University
Bozeman, MT

CONSULTANTS

Assessment:
Mary Hamm
Associate Professor
Department of Elementary Education
San Francisco State University
San Francisco, CA

Cognitive Development:
Pat Guild, Ed.D.
Director, Graduate Programs in Education and
Learning Styles Consultant
Antioch University
Seattle, WA

Kathi Hand, M.A.Ed.
Middle School Teacher and Learning Styles Consultant
Assumption School
Seattle, WA

Earth Science:
David G. Futch
Associate Professor of Biology
San Diego State University
San Diego, CA

Dr. Shadia Rifai Habbal
Harvard-Smithsonian Center for Astrophysics
Cambridge, MA

Tom Murphree, Ph.D.
Global Systems Studies
Monterey, CA

Suzanne O'Connell
Assistant Professor
Wesleyan University
Middletown, CT

Sidney E. White
Professor of Geology
The Ohio State University
Columbus, OH

Environmental Education:
Cheryl Charles, Ph.D.
Executive Director
Project Wild
Boulder, CO

Gifted:
Dr. James A. Curry
Associate Professor, Graduate Faculty
College of Education, University of Southern Maine
Gorham, ME

Global Education:
M. Eugene Gilliom
Professor of Social Studies and Global Education
The Ohio State University
Columbus, OH

Life Science:
Wyatt W. Anderson
Professor of Genetics
University of Georgia
Athens, GA

Orin G. Gelderloos
Professor of Biology and Professor of Environmental Studies
University of Michigan—Dearborn
Dearborn, MI

Donald C. Lisowy
Education Specialist
New York, NY

Dr. E.K. Merrill
Assistant Professor
University of Wisconsin Center—Rock County
Madison, WI

Literature:
Dr. Donna E. Norton
Texas A&M University
College Station, TX

Macmillan/McGraw-Hill School Division
10 Union Square East
New York, New York 10003
Printed in the United States of America

ISBN 0-02-274282-4 / 7

2 3 4 5 6 7 8 9 RRW 99 98 97 96 95 94 93

Activities!

EXPLORE

TRY THIS

Features

Links

Literature Link

Social Studies Link

Health Link

CAREERS

SCIENCE TECHNOLOGY AND Society

Focus on Technology

Focus on Technology

Focus on Environment

Departments

Changes In Matter

Every object in the universe—whatever its size, shape, color, or hardness—has one thing in common. Stars, planets, rocks, water, air, and all living things are made of the same fundamental material.

People have been curious about what things are made of for thousands of years. In fact, as far back as 2,500 years ago, the ancient Greeks tried to come up with a system that would help them classify all the matter in the world so they could understand the things around them. For a long time, most Greeks believed there was a simple explanation for all the different forms of matter, and that the four basic elements of soil, air, fire, and water made up the universe. According to this view, all matter consisted of one or more of these four elements.

However, the Greek philosopher Democritus (dǝ mä' kri tus'), developed another theory of matter. He challenged the old concept of matter by asking a new question that no one had thought of before. What would happen, he wondered, if you should cut a piece of iron into smaller and smaller pieces until you could no longer see it? Democritus hypothesized that eventually you would end up cutting the iron into such a small piece (or particle) that it could no longer be cut. Democritus called these tiny particles "atoms" (from the Greek words *a,* meaning "not," and *temnein,* meaning "to divide"). Although Democritus was correct in determining that all matter is composed of atoms, he mistakenly believed that there were different kinds of atoms for each material.

Greek symbols for air, Earth, fire, and water

Scientists in India had another understanding. While they accepted the idea that all matter was created from just a few elements, the Indian scientists developed an atomic theory of their own between A.D. 300 and A.D. 1000. These ancient scholars did not have advanced tools, such as microscopes, to study matter, but they suggested that each type of element has its own class of atoms that could not be divided into smaller units. This atomic theory was the first one that attempted to explain the ways in which different types of matter could react with each other, through an examination of cause and effect.

It has only been within the last 200 years that modern science has developed the tools to test the theory of existence of the many different types of atoms that make up matter. In 1803, British chemist John Dalton set forth a theory that matter consists of atoms of various weights that interact in accordance with specific principles. This discovery helped set the pattern for the periodic table of elements that you will study later in this unit.

Dalton's theory—matter is composed of atoms; atoms of the same element are identical; atoms of different elements are not alike; and atoms combine in simple ratios to form compounds.

ELEMENTS

Hydrogen 1	Strontites 46
Azote 5	Barytes 60
Carbon 54	Iron 38
Oxygen 7	Zinc 56
Phosphorus 9	Copper 56
Sulphur 13	Lead 90
Magnesia 20	Silver 190
Lime 24	Gold 190
Soda 28	Platina 190
Potash 42	Mercury 167

Minds On! You may have a good idea of what matter is already. Draw a line down the center of a piece of paper in your *Activity Log* on page 1. Label one column "Matter" and the other column "Not Matter." Take a few minutes to look around you. List each thing you observe in the classroom in one column or the other.

Think about what all the things you listed as matter have in common. For example, they have mass and take up space. Desks, books, chalk, the teacher, fellow students, light fixtures, clothes, and a clock on the wall all are objects around you that take up space.●

What objects did you list under the heading "Not Matter" in the Minds On? Did you list sounds you heard? Did you include time on your list? A shadow? What about sunlight? Did you list the chill or warmth you may have felt near a window? Are these things matter, or are they caused by matter? What about things like dust and clouds? Think about the composition of these objects.

What about air? You can't see, smell, or taste it. But we know it's there when we feel a breeze or see flags flying. In the following Try This Activity, you will determine if air can be classified as matter.

Wood is still wood when it is cut.

Activity!

Is Air Matter?

In this activity you will observe a property of air to determine if air is made up of matter.

What You Need

plastic glass, larger container of water, textbook, quart-sized plastic storage bag, table, string, *Activity Log* page 2

In your *Activity Log,* predict what will happen if you push the glass straight down into the container of water. Take the glass and turn it upside-down. Now push it straight down into the container of water. Does water fill the glass? Why or why not? Turn the glass sideways under the water. What happens? What does this tell you about the air that was in the glass?

In your *Activity Log* predict what will happen if you place a book on an inflated plastic storage bag. Now, take a quart-sized plastic storage bag and blow in it until it is filled with air. Tie the end of the bag to trap the air inside. Observe and record what happens when you place a book on the inflated bag. Will the bag without air support the book off the table? What property of air allows it to support the book?

Burning wood changes it into a different material.

Science in Literature

When did humans first begin to think about matter and test what they thought? When did scientists begin to suspect atoms existed? How can you learn about matter? You can experience it, touch it, observe it—but you can also read what others have to say about it.

Our Atomic World
by Melvin Berger.
New York: Franklin Watts, 1989.

You've heard about atoms, elements, and nuclear fusion. But what about red, blue, and green quarks and particle zoos containing "wild beasts"? Give up? They're all part of *Our Atomic World*. Melvin Berger's book touches on new developments and theories as well as human efforts over more than 2,000 years, to understand the nature of the atom. For inquisitive readers, kitchen-table experiments on matter and compounds are included.

Frozen Fire

by James Houston.
New York: Aladdin Books, 1977.

Matthew Morgan and his Inuit friend, Kayak, set out on a snow-mobile to locate Matt's father, who has not returned from a helicopter flight. During their hazardous Arctic adventure—partially based on a true story—they utilize Inuit knowledge about the properties of ice and snow to survive.

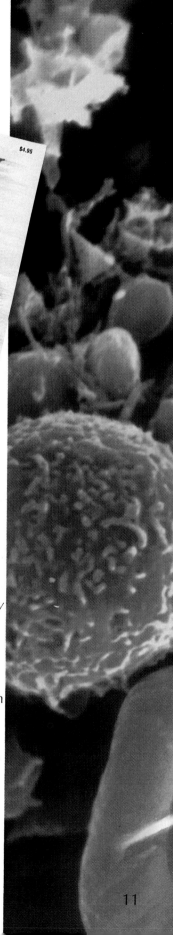

Other Good Books To Read

Pioneers of Science and Discovery: Ernest Rutherford and the Atom by P.B. Moon. Great Britain: Wayland, 1979.

Professor Moon, a research student of Ernest Rutherford, takes a detailed and affectionate look at the life of a man called "One of the Greatest Experimental Scientists of all Time."

Consumer Chemistry Projects for Young Scientists by David E. Newton. New York: Franklin Watts, 1991.

This book suggests investigations that can be made on common products, such as soap, shampoos, and toothpaste. The projects are intended to be conducted in a science laboratory under the guidance of a science teacher.

Einstein Anderson Makes up for Lost Time by Seymour Simon. New York: The Viking Press, 1981.

Adam "Einstein" Anderson knows science. In this book, Adam solves problems in everyday living by using his scientific knowledge. Each challenge is presented as a puzzle, giving readers a chance to test their scientific understanding.

Physical Properties

Ice melts in the warmth of sunlight. The melted water boils on the stove and turns to steam. It also freezes into ice again in the freezer. That same ice can be melted again. Does all matter exist in three forms? What causes matter to change from one form to another form?

Matter can exist in the form of a solid, liquid, or gas, depending on the temperature and pressure. Water exists in these three forms at normal Earth temperatures and pressures. Specific temperatures help us identify and classify water as a type of matter that is different from other types of matter. Let's think about some other physical properties of matter.

Minds On! Imagine that you have just met a friendly, and hungry, little alien who came to your classroom from another solar system. You invite her to the cafeteria with you for a bowl of ice cream, but she has never heard of ice cream and asks you to describe it for her. What would you say? Write the answer in your *Activity Log* on page 3, carefully describing the properties of color, texture, taste, and temperature.●

The way an object looks, feels, smells, tastes, melts, or freezes makes it different from every other object. We can use these properties to distinguish one type of matter from another.

The properties of an object, such as its structure and composition, also determine its use. That's why bridges are built with concrete and steel instead of glass and rubber. Can you imagine what would happen if a bridge trestle made of rubber began to melt and change shape on a hot summer day? Other materials have properties that make them practical to use in building aircraft. The airline industry wants to use aircraft with reduced weight to save energy. It uses lightweight metals in the construction of airplanes and helicopters, which reduces the amount of fuel required to fly them. At other times the odor of a substance is a desirable property. For example, chemists use the fragrance of lilacs to make some perfumes and air fresheners because that scent is pleasant to our noses.

All matter has certain properties that allow us to distinguish one type of material from another. In the following Explore Activity, we will investigate one of these properties.

Water is the only substance that can be a solid, liquid, or gas within the normal range of Earth's temperatures.

13

Activity!

If It's Dense, Will It Get to the Top?

In this activity you will investigate how a specific property of matter allows you to distinguish one substance from another.

What You Need

narrow, tall, glass jar
blue food coloring
100 mL each of corn oil, baby oil,
   corn syrup, and water
spoon
eraser
cork
small candle
Activity Log pages 4–5

What To Do

1 Measure 100 mL of water into the glass jar, and add 2 drops of food coloring.

2 Measure out 100 mL of corn oil, and slowly pour the corn oil down the spoon into the water.

3 Repeat the process in step 2 with 100 mL each of the baby oil and then the corn syrup.

What Happened?

1. How did the different liquids appear together in the cylinder?
2. In what order were the liquids arranged? In your *Activity Log,* draw and label an illustration that shows which liquids appeared on top, in the middle, and on the bottom.

What Now?

Think about how solid objects might interact when mixed with the liquids. Hypothesize what would happen if you dropped a small rubber eraser into the jar. Try it. What about a piece of cork or a birthday candle?

Physical Properties of Matter

In the Explore Activity, you found that some objects float on top of others because of the property of density. **Density** is defined as the amount of mass per unit volume of matter. The **mass** of an object is the amount of matter it contains. **Volume** is the amount of space an object occupies. In the activity you used equal volumes of each liquid. However, the mass of each volume of liquid was different and, therefore, their densities were not the same. The corn syrup had more mass and was, therefore, more dense. It sank to the bottom of the jar. The water has less mass than the corn syrup, but it has more mass than the corn oil, so it made a layer in between. The baby oil—the substance with the least mass—floated on top.

This grain ship floats because the combined density of the hull and the air inside it is less than the density of water.

When you added a piece of cork and an eraser to the layered liquids, you discovered that the piece of cork floated on the surface of the water, while a small eraser sank to the bottom of a layer of corn syrup. The cork is less dense than the water and the corn oil. The eraser is more dense than water and the corn syrup.

Would you expect a piece of iron to float if you dropped it into water? The density of iron is much greater than the density of water, so it wouldn't float. This doesn't mean that a sample of iron always has more mass than a sample of water. To say that iron has a greater density than water means that a given volume of iron will always have a greater mass than an equal volume of water.

Will a balloon filled with air float on water? Air is much less dense than water, and so the balloon will float on the water. Density is one characteristic of matter that we refer to as a physical property. A **physical property** is a property or characteristic of a substance—an element or compound—that can be observed without changing the nature of the substance. Mass and volume are physical properties. For example, we can measure the mass and volume of a sugar cube without changing it into something other than sugar. Another property of sugar is that it will burn. But if we burn a sugar cube, the sugar cube is no longer sugar. It is now another substance. Therefore, burning isn't a physical property, it's a chemical property. We'll discuss chemical properties in Lesson 2. There are many other physical properties besides mass, volume, and density that we use to identify objects, including, for example, color and shape. How do you use color and shape to help you identify objects? Think about the colors and shapes of various safety signs and symbols. Their distinctive colors or shapes are like the physical properties of materials that enable us to decide what uses can be made of them. In the Try This Activity on this page, let's use some everyday materials to examine the property of density.

TRY THIS
Activity!

Give Me an Egg Float, Please

This activity will demonstrate why it's easier to float in the ocean than in a swimming pool.

What You Need
500-mL beaker, water, fresh egg, measuring spoon, salt, spoon, *Activity Log* page 6

Fill a 500-mL beaker with water, and carefully put a fresh egg in the cup. Will the egg float or sink? Can you think of a reason why the egg behaves the way it does in the water? Now remove the egg. Add 4 Tbsp. of salt to the water while you stir until all the salt is dissolved. Predict whether the egg will do the same thing in salt water that it does in unsalted tap water. Put the egg in the liquid and watch what happens. Can you think of a reason why the egg responds the way it does? Write your observations and conclusions in your *Activity Log*. Density is one physical property of matter. Think about some other useful physical properties.

The manufacturing and painting of a traffic sign illustrates some of the physical properties of the metal used in producing it.

Minds On! Imagine that you have just gotten out of school and are preparing to retrieve your bike from the bike rack. Suddenly you see that there are ten red bikes all in a row that look like yours. How could you distinguish your bike from the others? What senses would you use, in addition to sight, to help you identify your bike? Could you feel a difference in the weight of the bike? Would the measurements, the weight, the dents and scratches on the frame, or the texture of the seat help you identify it? What about sound? Would you listen for the telltale squeak of brakes that need oiling? In your *Activity Log* on page 7, write a list of some of the ways you could test all the bikes to determine which one is yours.●

The texture of a material—whether it is rough, grainy, or smooth—is another physical property of matter. So is the odor of a substance. By smell, it's usually easy to tell if you are having fish or liver for dinner when you walk through your front door. It's also easy to know if there is a gas leak in your house, because the natural gas you use in your home has a distinctive odor added to it.

Hardness is also a physical property. It's used to classify minerals and gems. For example, diamonds are the hardest minerals, and talc is one of the softest minerals.

The properties of a material determine how the material can be used. For example, aluminum is less dense than iron. Therefore, it is used to make lightweight backpack frames and camping cookware. On the other hand, deep-sea research vessels are made of steel instead of aluminum, because steel is better able to withstand the water pressure far beneath the ocean.

States of Matter

Depending on its temperature, water and other materials may exist as a solid, a liquid, or as a gas. These conditions are called states of matter. States of matter are physical properties because the original substance has not changed. An iron nail is a solid having a

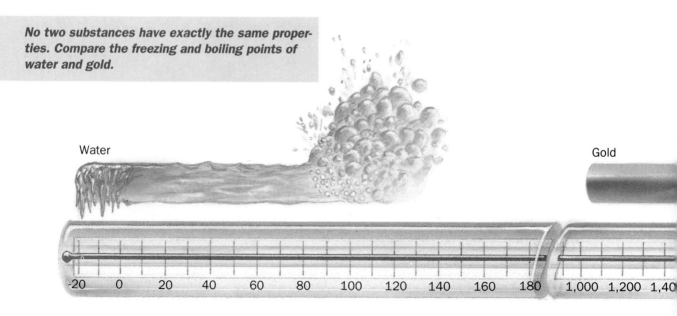

No two substances have exactly the same properties. Compare the freezing and boiling points of water and gold.

Water

Gold

-20 0 20 40 60 80 100 120 140 160 180   1,000 1,200 1,40

Degrees Celsius

definite shape and volume. When you melt the nail, it becomes liquid iron and it has no definite shape, but it still has almost the same volume. Because liquid iron has no definite shape, we can pour it into a container and it will take on the shape of the container. Solid iron, on the other hand, will retain its shape no matter what shape container we put it in. Think about a box of nails. Each nail does not conform to the shape of the box. If you were to strike the nail hard enough with a hammer, you may cause the nail to bend or change its shape. Both the solid and liquid iron will keep their volumes, however, no matter what size container you put them in.

Think about what happens when water is boiled or evaporates. It changes from a liquid to a gas—water vapor.

As a gas, water vapor can spread throughout a room or stay in a small column if it is kept in an airtight container. Thus, water vapor, like all gases, has no definite shape or volume. A gas takes on the shape and volume of whatever container it is in.

The temperature of a particular type of matter can determine whether it exists as a solid, liquid, or gas. Water turns into ice if the temperature falls below its freezing point, and water becomes a vapor if the temperature rises to its boiling point. Freezing point and boiling point are two other physical properties of matter. Most types of matter have their own specific temperatures at which they freeze and boil. When you think of water, you probably think of the liquid because that is the state it is in at room temperature. A piece of gold, on the other hand, is a solid at room temperature. You would have to heat it to a much higher temperature to make it become a liquid or gas. You can say that if the temperature of a material is above its freezing point, the material is a liquid. If the temperature is above the material's boiling point, it is a gas. Water is the only substance that we commonly find in all three states. In the Try This Activity on the next page, you can investigate water's three states.

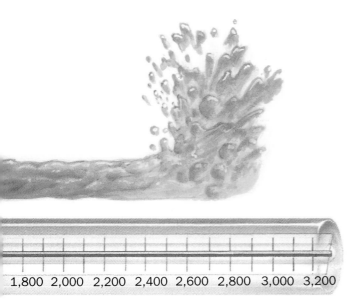

1,800 2,000 2,200 2,400 2,600 2,800 3,000 3,200

Literature Link
Frozen Fire

In the book, *Frozen Fire*, Matthew Morgan follows a frozen river to a point where he finds flowing water and water vapor, in the form of fog. Because of its physical properties, water is sometimes found in nature as a solid, a liquid, and a gas.

Matt and his Inuit buddy, Kayak, survive because they cooperate and share knowledge from their special cultures. After reading *Frozen Fire*, write some ideas in your **Activity Log** on page 8 that you might suggest if you were with them on their Arctic adventure.

Activity!

Presto Chango!

You can conduct an observation to determine the temperatures at which water changes from one state to another.

What You Need

thermometer, pan, ice, water, hot plate, goggles, *Activity Log* **page 9**

Place the thermometer in the pan filled with ice and some water. Observe and record in your *Activity Log* the temperature of the water. What is the temperature of the ice as it melts into a liquid? *Safety Tip:* Wear safety goggles and be very careful with the boiling water in this step. Slowly heat the beaker or pan of water until it begins to boil. Observe and record in your *Activity Log* the freezing and boiling temperatures of water.

How Does the Temperature of a Material Determine Its State?

All matter is made up of atoms. In solids, these tiny particles are bound quite close together by an attracting force that allows them to move only slightly back and forth. When the solid is heated and energy is added, the particles in the solid start to move more vigorously. The particles gain enough energy to overcome the attracting forces between the particles so that the particles can move about somewhat more freely. When this happens, the material becomes a liquid. As the liquid is heated, energy is being added to its particles, and the particles move faster and faster. When sufficient energy has been added to overcome all of the attractions between the particles, the particles move far enough apart so that the liquid becomes a gas in which the particles move about freely and very rapidly.

The fact that the particles in liquids and gases move about more freely than those in solids explains why liquids and gases take the shapes of their containers. It also explains why solids and liquids are much denser than gases.

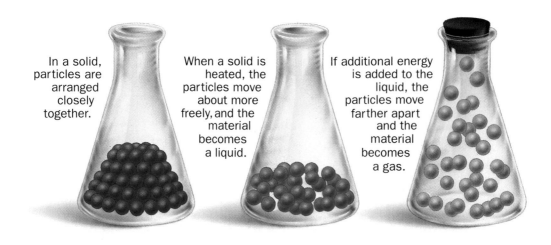

In a solid, particles are arranged closely together.

When a solid is heated, the particles move about more freely, and the material becomes a liquid.

If additional energy is added to the liquid, the particles move farther apart and the material becomes a gas.

Can you think of other physical properties of matter that might affect how a certain material is used? How about an object's boiling point, freezing point, hardness, or conductivity? How well a material conducts heat and how well it conducts electricity are two other physical properties of matter. Materials that readily allow heat and electricity to move through them are conductors. Materials that resist the flow of heat and electricity are insulators. The physical property of conductivity is important because it helps us determine the materials that are best for transmitting electricity or heat when we are trying to save energy.

Insulating material

Conducting material

The physical properties of certain materials make them useful for construction purposes.

Using the Physical Properties of Materials

The physical properties of materials determine the uses we find for them. For example, artists must consider the physical property of texture in choosing the kinds of paint they use to create landscapes, portraits, and other pictures. Acrylic, oil-based, and watercolor paints all have unique properties that affect how they interact with the canvas to produce the look artists want.

The ability of one kind of matter to dissolve into another is a physical property that an artist must keep in mind if he or she wants to use different types of paint in the same work. The consistency of paint is one more important property an artist must know about in order to work with the material. Most paint is at its best consistency when it appears buttery in texture. An experienced artist can reduce the consistency of paint by adding just the right amount of thinner to it on the palette. If the paint is too thin, the artist may make it stiffer by placing it on a piece of blotting paper before use.

Can you think of any other physical properties that artists might need to consider as they produce art? What about the porosity of the materials they are painting? Porosity is the ratio of the volume of a substance's pores—through which fluids, air, or light may pass—to its total volume. The more porous a material is, the more paint the substance will hold. How might this affect what happens to paint as it is applied to a porous material such as sandstone, compared to a nonporous substance such as iron? The more porous a material is, the more likely it is that a lot of paint will seep through the pores instead of adhering to the surface of the material.

These physical properties of matter affect not only what a painting looks like immediately after it is finished, but also how well a painting lasts over time. The different layers of fabric and sealing glue in an oil painting contract and expand as a result of temperature changes. This can change the appearance of old paintings, because they have been exposed to more temperature variations than newer paintings.

Artists coat their canvases with gesso—a mixture of gypsum and glue—prior to painting on them, to reduce the porosity of the canvas to paint.

Focus on Technology

Seashells to Ceramics

Why do you think electrical wiring is often made with copper rather than glass? Why is cookware usually made of metal, glass, or ceramic materials rather than plastic? Ceramics are products made from nonmetallic minerals. Because of their physical properties, ceramic objects conduct heat better than plastic. Plastic also melts and does not hold its shape well at high temperatures.

As good as human-made ceramics are at conducting heat, however, nature has a better way to make ceramics with physical properties far superior to anything we can produce in a laboratory. In the field of materials science, researchers are observing ordinary seashells to find out how to improve ceramics for a variety of uses. Scientists at Pacific Northwest Laboratories in Washington are studying mollusks, such as the nautilus and abalone, to see how their hard, shatter-resistant shells are grown.

The scientists have discovered how these mollusks' shells differ from ceramics made in a laboratory. These animals create high-quality ceramics by producing polymers (pä' li mûrz) in their shell-manufacturing cells. Polymers contain huge molecules formed when many smaller molecules and atoms are linked.

In the future, the researchers plan to use what they have learned about the physical properties of the mollusks to create artificial bone and nonrusting building materials. They are also attempting to grow high-temperature, superconducting ceramics by employing the same process the mollusks have used to make

seashells for more than 600 million years. Superconducting ceramics can conduct electricity more efficiently and with less energy loss than ordinary conductors. These superconducting ceramics now under development may have important applications in the fields of computers, nuclear energy, and physics. It's intriguing that these advancements in technology are being made possible from physical properties of mollusks.

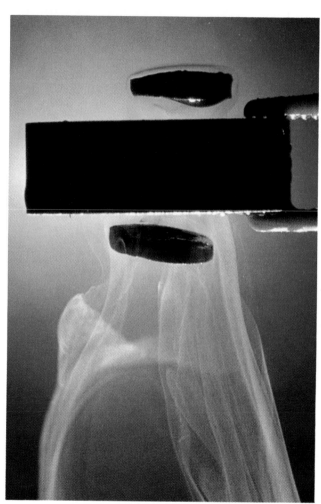

Superconductors are ceramics—brittle, glass-like materials—that lose all their electrical resistance at temperatures below −168 °C.

The koala bear of southeastern Australia depends on the physical properties of eucalyptus trees for food.

Human beings are not the only creatures that depend on the different physical properties of matter to obtain food and shelter. Many animals are instinctively aware of what kinds of materials possess the physical properties they need to survive.

Nature is filled with examples of organisms that depend almost exclusively on the properties they find in other organisms. For instance, the koala bear of southeastern Australia feeds only on the leaves and flowers of a certain species of eucalyptus tree.

Koalas use the eucalyptus tree for protection as well as food. They spend most of their time in the high branches of the trees so predators can't reach them, and they may stay in the same tree for several days. This animal is perfectly adapted to its environment. It grows to a maximum length of roughly 76 centimeters (2.5 feet) and it has large "hands" and "feet" with five toes each, including two opposable toes. The koala bear also has a sharp claw at the end of each toe to help it hang onto tree limbs. There are several physical properties of the eucalyptus tree that make it an ideal habitat for koalas. For example, the mature leaves of the tree are long, narrow, and leathery, so they conceal the animal from predators as it sleeps in the fork of two branches during the day. Since wild koala bears do not drink water, they get most of their liquids from eating the leaves and young shoots of the eucalyptus tree. *Koala* comes from an Australian Aborigine word meaning "no drink."

The physical properties of the koala bear are so well-suited for the physical properties of the eucalyptus tree that the animal can sleep curled up in the branches without relaxing its grip on the wood. Koala bears are marsupials, meaning that the females carry their young in a pouch, and they tend to remain in one area for as long as there is food available. These passive animals will not leave, even when kept in unfenced eucalyptus groves.

Sum It Up

We can see, hear, smell, touch, and taste different physical properties of matter to distinguish one substance from another. These physical properties are determined by the internal structure and arrangement of the parts of the material. This information is useful to the average person because it allows you to select the proper materials to use in your everyday activities. Every time you turn on a light switch, you depend on the conductivity of the wiring to carry an electric current to the light bulb. If you are making pasta for dinner, you cook it in water because you know that the boiling point of water is the right temperature to cook the noodles. When you are painting a picture, you try to get just the right consistency and texture of paint so that it doesn't run or smear on the canvas. And when you paddle a canoe, you rely on the density of the aluminum or wood in the canoe to be less than that of the water so you do not sink. All of these things—the conductivity, density, consistency, texture, and boiling point of a substance—are physical properties of matter that are important in your everyday life. Can you think of how any other physical properties you have studied affect you and determine why certain materials are used for specific purposes?

Using Vocabulary

density
mass
physical property
volume

Using the vocabulary words in this lesson, explain how an ore boat made out of heavy steel is able to float.

Critical Thinking

1. How might physical properties of matter be important to a detective searching a crime scene?

2. A block of wood has a density of 2.5 g/cm^3. The density of water is 1 g/cm^3. Will the block float in water? Why?

3. What must a submarine be able to do in order to submerge?

4. Estimate the density of the human body. HINT: Think about swimming!

5. Why do liquids and gases take the shape of their containers?

Chemical Properties

Change is something we experience so often that sometimes we are not even aware when it's happening. We see seeds sprouting and plants growing in the soil. We bake a cake using flour, water, baking soda, and other ingredients. We digest food. Think about each of these changes for a moment. How are they alike and how are they different?

Minds On! In your *Activity Log* on page 10, write what would happen if you held an ice cube in a beaker over a flame. Compare and contrast this with what would occur if you held a piece of paper over that same flame. How do the materials and their reactions differ? Why do the two substances respond to the flame the way they do?●

When we completely burn a piece of paper, the ashes left behind after the burning are no longer paper. Some paper is changed into gases as well. Similarly, if your bike rusts, the surface metal is no longer the same material. It has different properties. The nutrients supplied to your body cells are different from the food you ate. What happened to these materials? In the following Explore Activity, you'll observe certain properties of matter, which determine how one substance can change into another substance with different properties.

Liquid oxygen and liquid hydrogen fuel the main engines of the orbiter.

Activity!

Test Tube Detective

In this investigation you are going to identify some chemical properties of matter, and then use these properties to identify an unknown sample.

What You Need

safety goggles
3 test tubes
apron
3 droppers
1 tsp. each of baking powder, baking soda, cornstarch, and baby powder
measuring spoon
5 mL iodine solution
5 mL vinegar
5 mL water
masking tape
marking pen
Activity Log pages 11–12

What To Do

1 Label your test tubes "vinegar," "water," and "iodine."

2 Put about 1/4 tsp. of baking powder into each test tube. To the first test tube, add a dropper of water. Observe what happens and make notes in your *Activity Log*.

3 To the second test tube, add a dropper of vinegar. Again, note your observations in your *Activity Log*.

Safety!

See the *Safety Tip* in step 4.

5 Rinse out the test tubes with water in an approved location. Repeat steps 2–4, using baking soda, then cornstarch, and then baby powder instead of the baking powder, in the three test tubes.

6 Your teacher will give you an "unknown" sample to test. Add water, vinegar, and iodine solution as you did before. Referring to the observations you made in your *Activity Log,* try to identify this "unknown" powder. Write your findings in your *Activity Log*.

4 To the third test tube, add a dropper of iodine solution. *Safety Tip:* Be careful not to touch or spill the iodine solution, because iodine is poisonous and will cause stains. Wash your hands if you get iodine on them. Record your observations in your *Activity Log*.

What Happened?

1. Describe what happened when you mixed the baking powder, baking soda, cornstarch, and baby powder with water, vinegar, and iodine solution. Were these combinations alike in any ways?
2. What is the identity of your "unknown" powder? How many properties helped you identify it? Were you able to tell what you had by looking at it? What else helped you decide? How did you use the properties to identify the unknown powder?

What Now?

You discovered that iodine and cornstarch have a distinct reaction that is indicated by a dramatic color change. What happened when you mixed the iodine with the baking powder? What happened when you mixed the vinegar with the baking powder? What do you think might be in the baking powder? HINT: Think about these reactions. Check the baking powder ingredients.

Chemical Properties of Matter

In the previous lesson, you investigated physical properties of matter, such as density, which can be used to identify a substance. Remember, you can observe physical properties without changing the substance—when water freezes it is still water. In the Explore Activity, you observed that a material can also be identified by properties that determine how one substance changes into another substance. Remember the difference between these two kinds of properties as you study the processes involving the ways these properties affect the interaction of two or more substances.

Do you remember the fizzing that resulted when you combined vinegar with baking soda? That is an example of how combining two materials (baking soda and vinegar) can create a third substance (carbon dioxide) through the interaction of the chemical properties of these two materials. Unlike the physical properties of matter, the chemical properties can determine whether one material will react with another to form a new material. The chemical properties of matter allow us to use different materials in different ways.

A **chemical property** describes how a substance can react with another substance to form a third substance. Iron reacts with oxygen and water to form rust due to the chemical properties of iron and oxygen. Milk turns sour because of its chemical properties. You can tell from the change in taste and smell that a different kind of matter is present than when the milk was fresh. If a material fails to interact with another material, that is also a chemical property. For example, because gasoline burns, we say that it is flammable. Brick, on the other hand, does not burn, so we say that it is non-flammable. Being nonflammable is a chemical property of brick, just as being flammable is a chemical property of gasoline.

Houses, cars, and ships are painted to protect their surfaces from rotting or rusting due to environmental exposure. These changes occur to these objects because of the chemical properties of wood and metal. Paint does not exhibit the same chemical properties as wood and metal so it reacts differently to the elements of the environment. The paint provides a physical barrier between the metal or wood and the corrosive effects of freezing rain, road salts, and seawater, preventing these sub-

Rust never sleeps. Unprotected metal surfaces corrode when exposed to oxygen and water.

stances from reacting with the environment to form different materials.

Iron pipes used in plumbing are coated with zinc to protect the iron from oxygen and water. Without the zinc coating, the chemical properties of the iron cause it to rust in the presence of oxygen and water. When this happens, a new compound—iron oxide—is produced. Like the formation of rust, fire is a chemical process called oxidation. Wood or paper will burn because of the chemical properties of these substances. A piece of copper dropped into nitric acid will cause a chemical reaction.

Think back to the physical properties of matter you observed in the previous lesson. When we change the physical properties of a material, as we do when we paint it, cut it, or cause it to change state, we do not change the basic matter itself. Wood is still wood after it has been painted. Iron is still iron after it has

been coated with zinc. However, when we burn paper or wood or explode fireworks, the type of matter is changed. It isn't the same substance.

When a piece of iron pipe rusts, the pipe breaks apart and will no longer support a structure or hold liquids. The iron in the pipe has become iron oxide. Iron oxide doesn't have the same chemical and physical properties as iron. The color change that occurred when you added iodine solution to cornstarch showed that a new material was produced. The iodine reaction is a classic test for starch. You can tell if a food contains starch by testing it to see if it reacts in this way with iodine. Whenever you observe a color change, the formation of a gas, or the formation of a new substance, as you will in the next activity, you should suspect that a chemical change has occurred.

Cars of the future—utilizing more plastic and composite materials—will probably be lighter, more fuel efficient, and less susceptible to rust and corrosion.

Plastic body panels on automobiles aren't affected by rain or snow or by sodium chloride, which is used for ice control on highways.

Using the Chemical Properties of Matter

Chemical properties of materials determine whether or not, and how, one material will interact with another material to form a new substance. Some chemical properties are undesirable. For example, some substances undergo a chemical change when they contact oxygen and water vapor in the air. One such substance is sodium. Sodium must be stored in oil, because if it comes into contact with water, it will react violently, sometimes even explosively!

Expensive materials are destroyed every year because of undesired chemical changes that occur in these materials. For example, steel structures such as bridges sometimes collapse as the metal they are made of rusts and weakens. Iron water pipes, automobiles, railroad tracks, and many other items will also wear away as the metal in these objects rusts.

Can you name other undesirable chemical properties of matter? What about the chemical property of wood that causes it to rot, or the chemical property that causes some substances, such as some medicines, to break down in the presence of sunlight?

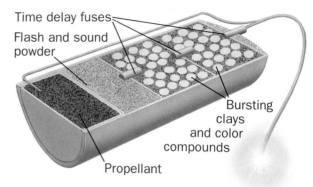

Fireworks all contain a quick fuse and a propellant to fire the shell from a launching tube. In the air, a time-delay fuse sets off the bursting charge that activates the light-emitting compounds.

Not all chemical properties of matter result in simple reactions such as the change in color that occurred when you added cornstarch to iodine solution. The results of combining the chemical properties of potassium nitrate, charcoal, and sulfur are literally explosive! The substance they form is commonly known as gunpowder. The chemical properties of gunpowder are valued for their use in producing the fireworks that entertain you on special occasions. As you read the feature on the next page, you will find out about some of the historical uses for the chemical properties of gunpowder.

TRY THIS Activity!

It's a Slow Way To Get Ready for a Picnic

Can the shell be removed from an egg without cracking it? In this activity you will conduct an experiment to find the answer.

What You Need

hard-boiled egg, uncooked egg, jar with lid, vinegar, *Activity Log* page 13

Place a hard-boiled egg in a jar and cover it with vinegar. Put a lid on the jar, and leave the egg in the vinegar overnight. The next day remove the egg from the vinegar, wash it off, and feel the shell. How does it feel? Hypothesize what properties of the eggshell and the vinegar cause the two substances to interact the way they do. Write your hypothesis in your *Activity Log*. Predict what would happen if you put an uncooked egg in the vinegar instead of the hard-boiled egg. Test your prediction.

Kaboom!

Have you wondered how long fireworks have been around and how they were invented? Fireworks have existed for thousands of years. In fact, the Chinese created the first simple fireworks, exploding pieces of bamboo in fires as long ago as 200 B.C. They discovered gunpowder more than 1,000 years ago, and by 1275, Chinese writer Wu Tzu-Mu (wü′ tsü′ mü′) was describing how *"the firecrackers made a glorious noise, which could be heard in the streets outside.*
. . . All the boats on the lake were letting off fireworks and firecrackers, the rumbling and banging of which was really like thunder."

The Chinese recognized the military applications of gunpowder even earlier. In 994, hundreds of years before Wu Tzu-Mu wrote about firecrackers, roughly 100,000 soldiers attacked the city of Tzu-t'ung (tsü′ tüng′) with gunpowder fire-arrows they shot from bows. These fire-arrows were said to be so destructive that they set fire to anything that would burn, including tents, food wagons, and stores of hay. The Chinese also learned that mixing powdered minerals or other materials into the gunpowder added color and bright sparkling effects to the explosions. They found that adding a small amount of sodium to the gunpowder caused a bright yellow-orange flame. If they added small amounts of copper, the resulting flame would be a brilliant blue. They also used the substances strontium and barium to produce red and green flames, respectively. These flame colors are chemical properties of these substances when they burn. Fireworks makers use their knowledge of the chemical properties of these substances to create colorful fireworks. Chemists use these properties to identify unknown metals. The actual chemical processes involved in these chemical changes

The colors of fireworks are produced by different substances— reds by strontium compounds, greens by materials containing barium, yellows by sodium, and blue-greens by copper compounds.

were largely unknown because a true study of pyrotechnics (pī′ rō tek′ niks), or the "science of fire," only emerged with modern advancements in chemistry. The modern field of pyrotechnics goes beyond the design of fireworks and includes research into hazard warning flares, safety matches, and the solid-fuel rocket boosters of the space shuttle

The chemical properties of materials are used in countless commercial applications every day. Bleach, for instance, not only helps us get our clothes clean but is also a vital ingredient in making paper. When the bleaching agent chlorine is added to paper pulp, a chemical change occurs in the pulp, causing its color to change to a bright white. Unfortunately, this process also produces new substances, such as dioxin. Dioxin is harmful to the environment and is suspected of causing some forms of cancer. Researchers at North Carolina State University recently developed a better way to manufacture paper. By working with the United States Environmental Protection Agency, the researchers found that paper mills can use the chemical properties of another substance, chlorine dioxide, instead of using chlorine. Chlorine dioxide slows down the bleaching process and reduces the harmful by-products of making paper by as much as 75 percent. The chlorine dioxide works more efficiently in bleaching pulps and produces a much smaller amount of the harmful substances if it is added to the pulp continuously and slowly in small portions, rather than being mixed in all at once. Some environmentalists are demanding that paper mills stop using chlorine as a bleaching agent altogether, but so far no practical substitutes for chlorine have been found. Using unbleached paper is one alternative to this problem. Many paper products are now available in both bleached and unbleached versions. Which would you choose if both products were available?

These photographs show several steps in the production of paper products. Notice the change in color of the paper pulp between steps 1 and 3, due to the bleaching action of chlorine dioxide.

Step 1

Step 3

Mechanical pulper

Fiber separation

Pulp washer

Bark removal

Screens

Drying rollers

Wire mesh

Reel of finished paper

Chemical pulper

Step 2

Pressure cooker

Vacuum

Squeezing rollers

Sum It Up

You investigated the chemical properties of some substances in this lesson. These properties refer to how matter changes as one type of material interacts, or fails to interact, with other materials to create a new substance. The interactions of chemicals are important because they can cause new substances to form with a whole new set of chemical and physical properties. You observed the changing texture and hardness of an eggshell as a result of being chemically changed by vinegar. You studied how some chemical properties are desirable while others are undesirable, and you learned of some ancient and modern uses of the special chemical properties of certain materials. As you proceed in this unit, you will consider what exactly makes up matter as well as learn how matter combines.

Using Vocabulary

chemical property

Pretend that astronauts have just returned from a faraway planet with a totally new substance. Write a brief paragraph describing its unusual chemical properties.

Critical Thinking

1. How are chemical properties different from physical properties?

2. Give an example of a physical and a chemical change.

3. Think about the Explore Activity on pages 28 and 29. What chemical reaction helped you identify substances containing starch?

4. Baking powder turned blue when it was mixed with iodine. What does this suggest about an ingredient of baking powder?

5. The wax in a candle first melts and then burns. What kind of properties are melting and burning?

Meet The Atom

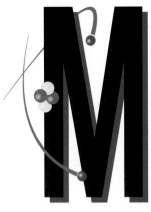

The Basic Building Blocks of the Universe

Much of our understanding of atoms has developed as a result of indirect observations, since we can't actually "see" atoms in action. This approach enables scientists to define the scale of atoms and describe their structure in a useful way, so that we can comprehend what atoms are, as well as how they make up matter.

Minds On! Have you ever looked closely at a full moon on a clear night? If you have, did you notice that some areas appeared bright while others were dark? Perhaps you saw the rough outline of a crater or two. If you could journey to the moon, how would the lunar surface look compared to the view you had from Earth?●

Since the moon has no atmosphere to block your vision, you might be able to make out some details of its landscape by the time you are halfway there. You can recognize that the bright and dark regions are large mountains and vast plains marked by craters. When you are near enough to the moon to pick out a landing site, you can begin to see even more distinctive features. You can inspect fields of boulders that might damage your lunar lander, and you can see smoother places where you would be able to land with less danger.

As you start to land, you can observe the texture of the ground. You might notice that it appears to be covered with a grainy dust or that it seems to be composed of solid rock. When you step onto the surface of the moon, you can closely examine the soil and you can see the fineness of the dust and flecks of different minerals in the rocks.

Now let's take an imaginary trip in the opposite direction. Imagine standing outside. What would it be like to slowly become smaller and smaller? What do you think you would see as you shrank in size until you were the same size as the pores and pits in the sidewalk?

The moon—our nearest space neighbor—as seen from Earth, 384,000 kilometers (240,000 miles) away

Does the surface look like sandpaper? As you become smaller, you see huge cracks that look like mountain ravines. The cracks soon seem to get larger until they resemble photographs of the Grand Canyon. As you diminish in size even more, you will find that the big cracks have little cracks in them. If you reach out to examine the solid walls of these cracks, you will find that the walls are made of tiny cloud-like blobs resembling a swarm of bees. You have reached the world of atoms!

Every time we breathe, we inhale billions of atoms. We lose some atoms when we exhale, others when we cry, and still more when we sweat. Atoms continue to move from person to person and from one substance to another. Atoms have been around since the beginning of time. Think about what this means! You may have atoms in your body that were once a part of an Antarctic glacier, a part of Einstein's brain, Beethoven's sheet music, or part of George Washington Carver or Marie Curie. Some of the atoms in your body may even have come from stars that exploded millions of years ago!

You know that all matter is made up of atoms, yet atoms are too tiny to be seen with even the best microscopes. How is it possible to demonstrate that something like an atom exists even though you can't see it? The next activity may give you some ideas.

The moon—made of the same materials as Earth—has no water or atmosphere, and its weather does not change.

Activity!

The Mystery Box

In this activity you will systematically investigate and describe matter that you cannot see.

What You Need

sealed container provided by your teacher
ruler
magnet
Activity Log **pages 14–15**

What To Do

1 Observe the shape of the container you are given. Record this and any other exterior details you believe are important in your *Activity Log*.

2 Make any measurements you think might help you describe the interior or contents of the container. Note these measurements in your *Activity Log*.

3 Carefully tilt the box. Shake it. Hold the magnet next to the box and run it back and forth across the surface. Make any observations you can. Write these in your *Activity Log*.

4 Make a hypothesis about the inside structure or contents of the box. Does it have separate compartments? Write the hypothesis in your *Activity Log,* and draw a picture of what you think the inside of the box looks like.

5 Compare your hypothesis with those of others in your group and with those of other groups.

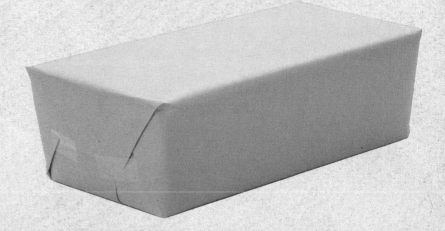

What Happened?

1. How did you develop your hypothesis about the interior structure of the sealed box? Did any articles in the box roll or slide about? Did anything inside the box seem to respond to the magnet?
2. If your tested hypothesis was not true, list any new hypothesis you developed about the interior structure of your box.
3. How well did your hypothesis hold up to the analysis of the other groups?

What Now?

1. How do you think this activity might compare to the way scientists proposed the idea that all matter is made up of atoms?
2. Do you think the theory that all matter is made up of atoms can ever be changed? Why or why not?

EXPLORE

39

In the mystery box activity, you developed a hypothesis about the inside structure of your box, based on the observations of your group. Our current understanding of the atom has developed in much the same way, as we have been able to observe more and more properties of matter during the past several centuries.

Inside the Atom

Atoms are extremely small. If you could lay atoms in a straight line, side by side, it would take about ten million atoms to extend over the length of one millimeter. And yet, even though atoms are so tiny, their presence can be detected with some advanced types of microscopes. Not only can atoms be detected, but scientists have discovered even smaller units that make up atoms.

John Dalton, an English chemist, proposed in 1803 that each chemical element is composed of single building blocks called atoms. He did not know there were smaller particles making up matter.

After Dalton explained his atomic theory, it was almost 100 years before scientists learned that the atom was not the smallest particle making up matter. Michael Faraday and other scientists conducted studies of electricity in the late 1800s that led to J. J. Thomson's discovery that very small, negatively charged particles, called **electrons,** were a part of all atoms. Electrons were found to be the same no matter what type of atom they were in.

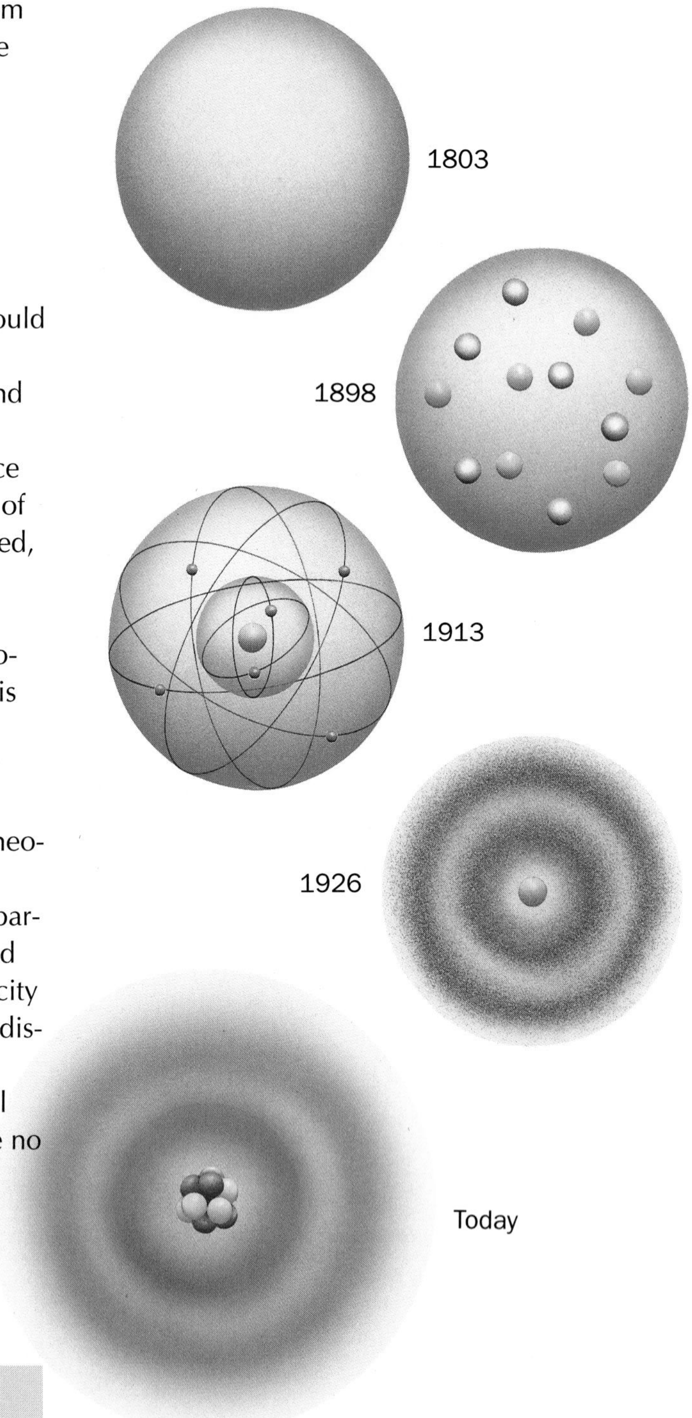

1803

1898

1913

1926

Today

Atoms have been visualized in different ways through the ages.

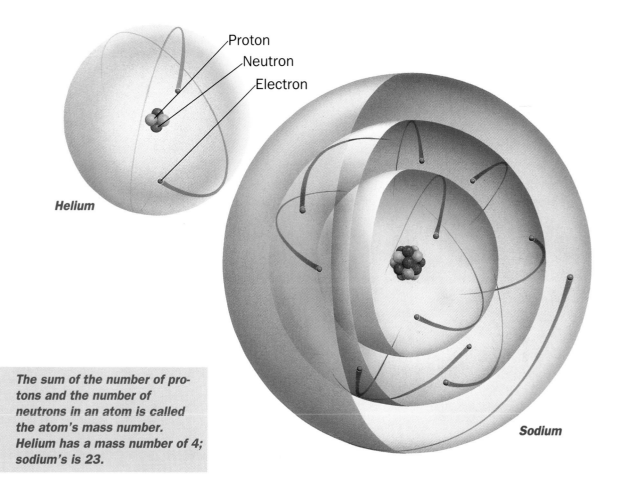

Proton
Neutron
Electron

Helium

Sodium

The sum of the number of protons and the number of neutrons in an atom is called the atom's mass number. Helium has a mass number of 4; sodium's is 23.

About the same time, Ernest Rutherford learned that atoms had a tiny, but very dense, positively charged center—a **nucleus.** He suggested that the atom included a nucleus with electrons traveling around it. If you enlarged the scale of an atom to the size of a large stadium, you would find that an atom is mostly empty space. The nucleus of our scaled-up atom could be represented by a pea on the 50-yard line. The electrons would probably be buzzing around the parking lot. They would be so tiny, you might not even notice them. The positive charge of the nucleus balances the negative charge of the electrons, and so the atom is neutral.

That's not all. Other scientists discovered two more parts to the atom, the proton and the neutron. The proton has a positive electrical charge, while the neutron, as its name implies, is neutral—it has no charge.

Both the proton and the neutron exist in the nucleus of an atom. They have about the same mass, and together they account for most of the mass of an atom. In fact, it would take roughly 1,835 electrons to equal the mass of one proton or one neutron. The electrons zip around the nucleus, forming a kind of "cloud" of negative charge.

Over time scientists continue to develop theories to explain the structure and behavior of the atom. For example, in 1955 physicist Maria Goeppert Mayer theorized that a nucleus consists of several shells, or orbital levels, with the arrangement of protons and neutrons in these levels producing a characteristic stablilty for each type of nucleus. Dr. Mayer and her colleagues shared the 1963 Nobel prize in Physics for their theoretical contributions.

The chemical and physical changes that matter undergoes can be explained in terms of these three units—electrons, protons, and neutrons.

Every atom can be identified by its atomic number. The **atomic number** of an atom is the number of protons the atom has in its nucleus; and since an atom is neutral, it is also the number of electrons. Hydrogen has only one proton in its nucleus, so its atomic number is 1. Oxygen, on the other hand, has an atomic number of 8. Gold has an atomic number of 79, and calcium, 20. No two elements have the same atomic number. Much as people are identified by their fingerprints or social security numbers, atoms are identified by their numbers of protons.

The **mass number** of an atom is the sum of the number of protons and the number of neutrons in the atom. It is called the mass number because, as was mentioned earlier, these two particles are responsible for almost all of the mass of an atom. The reason an atom has a mass number in addition to an atomic number is that two atoms of the same element will always have the same atomic number, but they can have different mass numbers. Atoms having the same number of protons—the same atomic number—but different numbers of neutrons are called **isotopes.** The element hydrogen has three isotopes. An atom of the most common form of hydrogen has one proton and no neutrons in its nucleus. Its mass number is 1. Another form of hydrogen, called deuterium (dü tîr' ē əm), has one proton and one neutron in its nucleus. The mass number of deuterium is 2. A third form of hydrogen—tritium (trit' ē əm)—has one proton and two neutrons in its nucleus, and its mass number is 3. Most of the 109 known elements have at least two known isotopes. In the next Try This Activity, you can demonstrate your understanding of atomic numbers and isotopes.

All atoms of an element have the same number of protons, but some—called isotopes—may have a different number of neutrons than others. Hydrogen has three isotopes—protium, deuterium, and tritium.

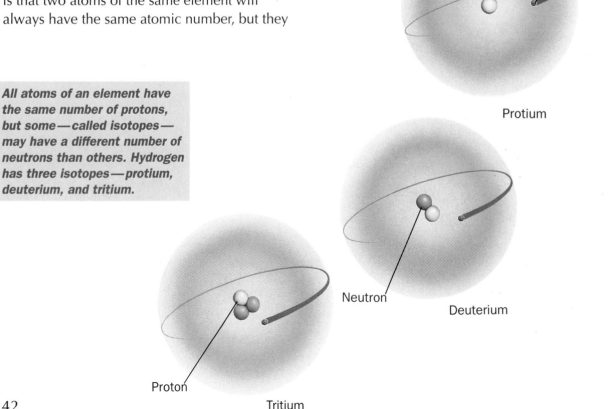

Electron

Protium

Neutron

Deuterium

Proton

Tritium

Activity!

Matter Modeling

Use your knowledge of the structure of atoms to determine the numbers of neutrons, protons, and electrons in three isotopes of magnesium.

What You Need

3 different colored pencils or pens
***Activity Log* page 16**

Magnesium—used to make airplanes because of its light weight—has an atomic number of 12. It has three isotopes that occur in nature. Complete the table in your ***Activity Log*** by filling in the correct numbers of protons, neutrons, electrons, and atomic mass numbers.

In your ***Activity Log,*** there are diagrams representing isotopes of magnesium. Label each diagram —using different colored pencils or pens—with the numbers of protons, neutrons, and electrons in each isotope.

When we use a pencil and paper to model the structure of atoms as you did in the Try This Activity, it is very difficult to understand how very small these particles really are. In the next Literature Link, you will gain some understanding of actual sizes.

Literature Link

Our Atomic World

If you read *Our Atomic World,* by Melvin Berger, you will learn about subatomic particles such as protons and neutrons. These particles are said to be only 0.000,000,000,000,001 m wide. In scientific shorthand we call this number 10^{-15}, to avoid writing all those zeros. Quarks—particles believed to make up protons and neutrons—are even smaller.

Considering what you have learned about our changing understanding of the atom since early times, hypothesize whether even smaller subatomic particles might still be discovered. Prepare and deliver a classroom presentation on your position.

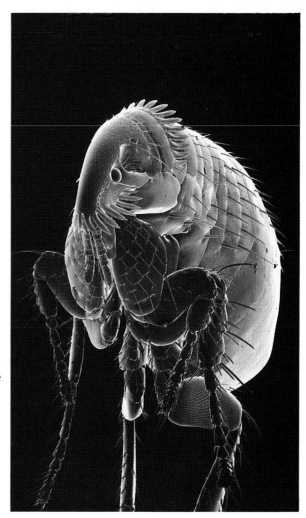

Atoms are made of even smaller particles. Could the tiny cat flea in this magnified photograph have smaller fleas of its own?

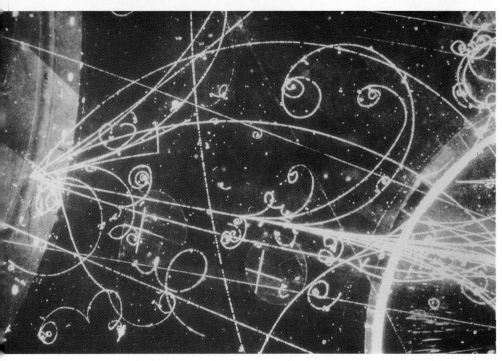

The paths of subatomic particles can be photographed in particle accelerators and colliders.

Space: the Final Frontier?

A popular television series in the 1960s began every episode with a narrator saying this line. Is space *really* the final frontier? Probably not—look at how little we know about the atom. You've been reading about the parts of an atom and how we study them, but what we don't know about atoms surely outweighs what we do know about them. What holds the protons and neutrons together in the nucleus of an atom? Can matter be turned into something else? These are only a few of the questions scientists are trying to answer. Fortunately, we now have the advanced technology to dig deeper into the secrets of the atom.

Ironically, some of the largest and most expensive scientific equipment on Earth is designed to study the tiny atom. Scientists have designed and built particle accelerators and colliders for one purpose—to smash the nucleus of an atom to see what subatomic particles result. The list of "atom-smashing" machines

includes the Large Electron-Positron collider in Europe, the Fermilab Accelerator in Illinois, and the Stanford Linear Accelerator Center in California. These machines enable scientists to observe properties of a subatomic particle called a quark, the particle that makes up the protons and neutrons in an atom's nucleus. They have also predicted the existence of a particle called a lepton. Leptons are believed to be related to the behavior of electrons. Scientists hypothesize that these subatomic units may hold the answer to the question of what forces hold the universe together.

Think back to the Explore Activity in which you tried to guess the structure inside the sealed box. Did you feel frustrated when you weren't allowed to open the box to find out for sure whether your hypothesis was correct? That's how the scientists who hypothesize about the internal structure of an atom sometimes feel. Maybe these sophisticated machines will allow them to "open the box" of the atom and look inside.

Sum It Up

When you performed the mystery box activity, you found that making observations isn't always easy—especially when we can't see what we are trying to observe. That is why models, using familiar ideas to explain unfamiliar things, have been useful in gaining an understanding of atoms. Models are especially helpful when you are studying atoms, which are so small that it takes more than 100 million of them to make a line 1 centimeter (.39 inch) long.

In recent decades, for the first time, humans have developed advanced particle accelerators able to probe the nature of matter on a scale far smaller than even atoms. Perhaps they will lead to breakthroughs in answering fundamental questions such as: What is the universe made of, and what are the forces that bind its parts together?

Using Vocabulary

atomic number   **mass number**
electrons   **nucleus**
isotopes

Using the vocabulary words in this lesson, write a short story on the atomic structure of an amazing new imaginary element that has just been discovered.

Critical Thinking

1. Explain why it is often said that matter is mostly empty space.

Use the periodic table on page 54 to help answer the following questions.

2. What element has 88 protons? How many electrons does this element have?

3. What is the atomic number of sodium? What is its mass number?

4. An element has an atomic number of 53 and an atomic mass of 127. How many neutrons does this element have? What is this element?

5. How are isotopes of the same element different?

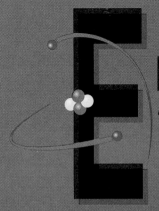

Elements
And The Periodic Table

All matter in the universe is made from only 109 elements. Each element is different from every other element. What are elements and how are they identified and classified?

Each element has its own unique properties, both chemical and physical, that determine the variety of uses for it. Gold, for example, is a beautiful, soft, and unreactive metal—one of very few metals that isn't silver-colored. Because of these properties, gold is used in art, jewelry, and dental work in spite of its cost and relative rarity. Another element, oxygen, is important because plants produce it during photosynthesis when they make their food, and all animals, including humans, need it to breathe. Oxygen can be found in Earth's atmosphere, and it is also a part of water and many other common materials. The element nitrogen, like oxygen, is found in Earth's atmosphere, and accounts for about 78 percent of the air we breathe. Nitrogen is part of the proteins in our bodies, and is found in plant fertilizers and explosives as well. Can you think of another substance that might contain nitrogen or oxygen?

Minds On! Think about the enormous task of classifying all 109 elements. How would you classify, for example, a large bag of various buttons? How would you group the buttons in your collection? What properties would you use to classify them? Could a button be in one group but also have features similar to those in another group? Describe the grouping plan you develop in your *Activity Log* on page 17.●

All matter is composed of combinations of only 109 elements.

47

Activity!

Classifying Through Conduction

In this activity you will demonstrate your knowledge of the properties of matter to classify substances into two basic groups.

What You Need

solid samples of aluminum, slate, copper, lead, plastic, and zinc conductivity tester
Activity Log **pages 18–19**

What To Do

1 Working in groups of two, obtain a small amount of each substance. Examine each sample carefully. Make a note of any physical properties you observe in your *Activity Log*.

2 Test each sample with the conductivity tester to determine if it conducts electricity. Record your observations in your *Activity Log*.

What Happened?

1. Which substances conducted electricity? Was there any common quality among the substances that displayed this physical property?

What Now?

1. Do the substances in each group share any other common physical properties?
2. How would you now group the substances based on the physical property of conductivity you just observed?

A variety of elements as they occur in nature

Everyday Elements

In the Explore Activity, you established that metals conduct electricity. What other tests would help you classify elements such as platinum, sulfur, hydrogen, mercury, and iron as metals or nonmetals, based on their physical properties? You've seen that metals can float when they've been spread out in shapes that give them an average density less than water. Yet in their natural state, most metal elements will sink. What about nonmetal elements? Would you expect hydrogen and carbon to float or sink in a body of water?

What other properties do metals have? Are they hard or brittle? Will they break when you hit them? Most metallic elements do not melt easily. Can you name an exception? (HINT: You might find it in a long, thin, silver tube.) Can you come up with any other ways to distinguish metal elements from nonmetal elements? Look around you. Examine what certain types of metals are used for, and then ask yourself what physical properties of those metals make them appropriate for the purpose they serve.

Minds On! Let's take a moment to think about some metals and see how their unique properties are used. Have you seen jewelry made from gold or silver? What properties of these materials make them useful in jewelry? List some other possible uses for these metals in your *Activity Log* on page 20.

Do you know what elements are used in coins? Look at pennies, nickels, dimes, and quarters. What properties of these elements make them useful as coins? Can you think of any properties of metals used in coins that make them suitable for use in vending machines? Could we use coins made of plastic or some other nonmetallic substance? Do you see any evidence that more than one metal was used in some of these coins? If so, make a diagram in your *Activity Log* of what you saw and hypothesize a reason. Compare your findings and predictions with other groups. Did you arrive at similar conclusions?●

So far in this lesson, we've mentioned a number of elements including gold, oxygen, carbon, and mercury. In addition to its name—which often has an interesting derivation—each element has a symbol that is often used to identify it. Many elements simply use the first letter of their English names. For example, carbon is C, hydrogen is H, oxygen is O, and uranium is U.

Minds On! Imagine that you've been asked to assign letter symbols for the following ten elements—carbon, hydrogen, helium, calcium, nitrogen, oxygen, nickel, neon, chlorine, and sodium. In your *Activity Log* on page 21, write down the simplest letter symbols you can for each element.●

Symbols for elements are usually made up of one or two letters, although a new system of naming recently discovered elements uses three-letter symbols. For elements that have names beginning with the same letter as other elements, a second letter has been added to the symbols. The addition of this second letter enables us to distinguish between calcium, copper, chlorine, chromium, and californium, which all start with *c*. Calcium is identified as Ca, chlorine is Cl, chromium is Cr, and californium is Cf. But what about the element copper? Its symbol is Cu, and there is no *u* in copper. So there must be some exceptions made to the rules when using symbols to represent elements.

Some of the elements that have been known for centuries have symbols taken from their ancient names. Copper takes its name from the island of Cyprus in the Mediterranean Sea. Since the Romans obtained most of their copper from the island, they called the metal *aes Cyprium* which means "bronze of Cyprus," but the Latin name for it is *cuprum,* hence the symbol Cu. Other elements were identified at a time when Latin was the language used in the schools, and many elements bear symbols derived from the Latin words for them.

Elements' Names

The names of the six newest elements that have been discovered are based on Latin and Greek words, and those names are formed by combining words for the atomic numbers of the elements. For instance, element 104 is called unnilquadium because *un* means "one," *nil* means "zero," and *quad* means "four."

The U.S. research team that discovered element 104 proposed that the new element be named Rutherfordium, honoring physicist Ernest Rutherford. Soviet scientists also claim to have created element 104 and propose it be named Kurchatovium, after Soviet physicist Igor Kurchatov. Neither claim of discovery or proposed name has been officially accepted.

Nobelium was named after Alfred Nobel, the inventor of dynamite and founder of the Nobel peace prize. Mendelevium was named for Dmitri Mendeleev (men' də lēv'). Californium and berkelium were named after the places where they were discovered. Now that you have some notion of how elements are named and symbols developed for them, let's consider how they can be classified.

Classifying Elements

Can you think of something that occurs periodically? What about a calendar? Each week in a month is similar. As you go from Sunday to Saturday, some "properties" repeat themselves. Fridays are always the last day of school for the week. Saturdays and Sundays are usually a time for family activities. All days of the week in a calendar are in vertical columns. All Sundays are in one group, Mondays in the next, and so on. In a similar way, January is always the first month of the year, and December is always the last. Martin Luther King Jr.'s birthday is celebrated in January, Labor Day always comes in September, Halloween in October, and Thanksgiving in November. As you will see, a calendar and a periodic table have similar patterns.

The periodic table has space to list new elements. Do you think there are any undiscovered elements?

Minds On! Suppose a new element is discovered with an atomic number of 110. Make up a name for this element based on the method used for actual elements such as element 104.●

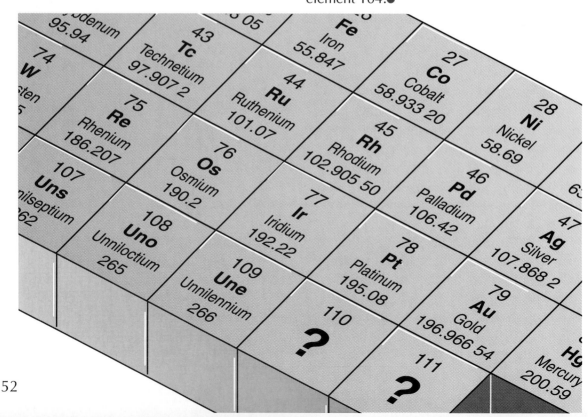

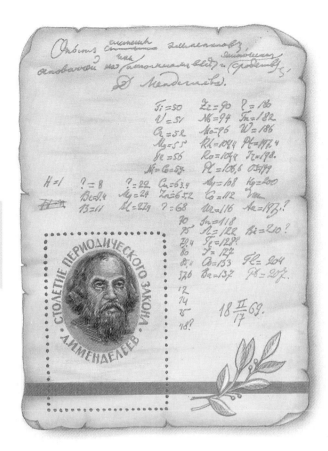

Mendeleev's table—first published in 1869—predicted the existence of two undiscovered elements. His predictions were confirmed when gallium was discovered in 1875 and scandium in 1879.

The Periodic Table

About 100 years ago, scientists developed a table of the elements, called the **periodic table,** to help group the properties of elements. The Russian chemist Dmitri Mendeleev proposed such a table in 1869. In this table he listed each element by its mass, with the least massive element first, then the next, and so on. The first elements on his table were hydrogen, helium, and lithium. However, instead of simply listing the elements in one continuous long line, he put the elements into vertical columns based on similar properties.

For example, the elements lithium and sodium are both soft, shiny metals that react explosively with water, so Mendeleev placed them in the same column in his table. The arrangement of elements was not exact, though, and there were some other elements with properties that did not fit in where their masses placed them. Mendeleev also did not know about all the elements because many had yet to be discovered. He left question marks in his table for unknown elements, and later was able to predict the properties of these undiscovered elements.

Henry Moseley, a young British physicist, came up with an answer to the problem of misplaced elements in 1913. Moseley found that, if arranged by their atomic numbers instead of their masses, the elements fit well into columns of similar properties. The name *periodic table* comes from the fact that if elements are categorized by their increasing atomic numbers, certain properties will repeat in a regular or "periodic" way. You will recall that the atomic number is the same as the number of protons in the nucleus of an atom. Knowing that, can you figure out the atomic number of an element, such as hydrogen, which has one proton? How about helium, which has two protons? The modern periodic table is displayed on pages 54–55.

THE PERIODIC TABLE
(based on Carbon 12 = 12.000)

Metals

Group							
1* **IA***							
2 **IIB**							

1 (Period 1)
1 **H** Hydrogen 1.007 94

2 (Period 2)
3 **Li** Lithium 6.941 | 4 **Be** Beryllium 9.012 182

3 (Period 3)
11 **Na** Sodium 22.989 768 | 12 **Mg** Magnesium 24.305 0

Group headers:
3 IVB | 4 IVB | 5 VB | 6 VIB | 7 VIIB | 8 | 9 VIIIB

4
19 **K** Potassium 39.098 3 | 20 **Ca** Calcium 40.078 | 21 **Sc** Scandium 44.955 910 | 22 **Ti** Titanium 47.88 | 23 **V** Vanadium 50.941 5 | 24 **Cr** Chromium 51.996 1 | 25 **Mn** Manganese 54.938 05 | 26 **Fe** Iron 55.847 | 27 **Co** Cobalt 58.933 20

5
37 **Rb** Rubidium 85.467 8 | 38 **Sr** Strontium 87.62 | 39 **Y** Yttrium 88.905 85 | 40 **Zr** Zirconium 91.224 | 41 **Nb** Niobium 92.906 38 | 42 **Mo** Molybdenum 95.94 | 43 **Tc** Technetium 97.907 2 | 44 **Ru** Ruthenium 101.07 | 45 **Rh** Rhodium 102.905 50

6
55 **Cs** Cesium 132.905 43 | 56 **Ba** Barium 137.327 | 71 **Lu** Lutetium 174.967 | 72 **Hf** Halnium 178.49 | 73 **Ta** Tantalum 180.947 9 | 74 **W** Tungsten 183.85 | 75 **Re** Rhenium 186.207 | 76 **Os** Osmium 190.2 | 77 **Ir** Iridium 192.22

7
87 **Fr** Francium 223.019 7 | 88 **Ra** Radium 226.025 4 | 103 **Lr** Lawrencium 260.105 4 | 104 **Unq** Unnilquadium 261 | 105 **Unp** Unnilpentium 262 | 106 **Unh** Unnilhexium 263 | 107 **Uns** Unnilseptium 262 | 108 **Uno** Unniloctium 265 | 109 **Une** Unnilennium 266

Lanthanoid Series
57 **La** Lanthanum 138.905 5 | 58 **Ce** Cerium 140.115 | 59 **Pr** Praseodymium 140.907 65 | 60 **Nd** Neodymium 144.24 | 61 **Pm** Promethium 144.912 8 | 62 **Sm** Samarium 150.36

Actinoid Series
89 **Ac** Actinium 227.027 8 | 90 **Th** Thorium 232.038 1 | 91 **Pa** Protactinium 231.028 88 | 92 **U** Uranium 238.028 9 | 93 **Np** Neptunium 237.048 2 | 94 **Pu** Plutonium 244.064 2

*Currently there are two systems of labeling groups on the table. A traditional system uses Roman numerals I through VIII with letters A and B. A more current system uses Arabic numerals I through 18 designations. Throughout this text the current system will be used with traditional heading following in parenthesis, for example, Group 1 (IA).

			18 VIIIA

			13 IIIA	14 IVA	15 VA	16 VIA	17 VIIA	18 VIIIA
								2 **He** Helium 4.002 602
			5 **B** Boron 10.811	6 **C** Carbon 12.011	7 **N** Nitrogen 14.006 74	8 **O** Oxygen 15.999 4	9 **F** Fluorine 18.998 403 2	10 **Ne** Neon 20.179 7
10	11 IB	12 IIB	13 **Al** Aluminium 26.981 539	14 **Si** Silicon 28.085 5	15 **P** Phosphorus 30.973 762	16 **S** Sulfur 32.066	17 **Cl** Chlorine 35.453 7	18 **Ar** Argon 39.948
28 **Ni** Nickel 58.69	29 **Cu** Copper 63.546	30 **Zn** Zinc 65.39	31 **Ga** Gallium 69.723	32 **Ge** Germanium 72.61	33 **As** Arsenic 74.921 69	34 **Se** Selenium 78.96	35 **Br** Bromine 79.904	36 **Kr** Krypton 83.80
46 **Pd** Palladium 106.42	47 **Ag** Silver 107.868 2	48 **Cd** Cadmium 112.41	49 **In** Indium 114.82	50 **Sn** Tin 118.710	51 **Sb** Antimony 121.75	52 **Te** Tellurium 127.60	53 **I** Iodine 126.904 47	54 **Xe** Xenon 131.290
78 **Pt** Platinum 195.08	79 **Au** Gold 196.966 54	80 **Hg** Mercury 200.59	81 **Tl** Thallium 204.383 3	82 **Pb** Lead 207.2	83 **Bi** Bismuth 208.980 37	84 **Po** Polonium 208.982 4	85 **At** Astatine 209.987 1	86 **Rn** Radon 222.017 6

63 **Eu** Europium 151.965	64 **Gd** Gadolinium 157.25	65 **Tb** Terbium 158.925 34	66 **Dy** Dysprosium 162.50	67 **Ho** Holmium 164.930 32	68 **Er** Erbium 167.26	69 **Tm** Thulium 168.934 21	70 **Yb** Ytterbium 173.04
95 **Am** Americium 243.061 4	96 **Cm** Curium 247.070 3	97 **Bk** Berkelium 247.070 3	98 **Cf** Californium 251.079 6	99 **Es** Einsteinium 252.082 8	100 **Fm** Fermium 257.095 1	101 **Md** Mendelevium 258.986 6	102 **No** Nobelium 259.100 9

Look at column 2 of the periodic table and note the elements beryllium, magnesium, calcium, strontium, barium, and radium. These metallic elements conduct electricity. Now, notice column 16. The elements listed there—such as oxygen and sulfur—are nonmetals. Since most nonmetals do not conduct electricity, you can infer that columns of elements on the periodic table have similar properties. These vertical columns are called **families** or **groups,** and the rows that run horizontally across the periodic table from left to right are called **periods.** The properties of elements gradually change across a period.

As you move from left to right across a period in the periodic table, the elements change from metals to nonmetals. For example, period 2 of the table lists lithium as element 3, a metal, while element 10, neon, is a nonmetal. If you inspect period 3, you will see that sodium is listed as element 11, a metal, and argon, element 18, is a nonmetal.

The activity of an element is determined by how easily it gains or loses electrons. Metals tend to lose electrons when they react with other elements. Nonmetals, on the other hand, tend to gain electrons. In the following Try This Activity, you will investigate activity between several metals.

TRY THIS

Activity!

Copper Caper

Here's your chance to transform an ordinary nail into a special one.

What You Need

rubber gloves, lab apron, safety goggles, 250-mL beaker, 1 Tbsp. copper sulfate powder, 150 mL warm water, stirring rod, copper wire, "D" cell, masking tape, copper strip, steel (common) nail—small size, wire cutter, *Activity Log* page 22

Put on the rubber gloves, lab apron, and safety goggles. Measure and pour 150 mL of warm water into the beaker. CAREFULLY add the copper sulfate powder to the water and stir gently until the powder dissolves. Cut two pieces of copper wire about 8 in. long. Use masking tape to tape one end of a wire to the copper strip. Wrap one end of the second piece of wire around the head of the nail, and twist it tightly to secure it. Use masking tape to fasten the wire from the copper strip to the positive (+) post of the battery. On a "D" cell , this is the top. Be sure the wire doesn't touch the other post of the battery. Use another piece of tape to secure the wire with the nail attached to the negative (−) post of the battery. This will be the bottom of the "D" cell. Insert the nail into the solution in the beaker. Make sure the solution covers the nail. Insert the copper strip into the solution in the beaker. The strip does not need to be covered with the solution. Do not allow the masking tape to be touched by the solution.

After the activity is completed, follow your teacher's instructions for disposal of the solution.

Answer the following questions in your *Activity Log.* What color is copper when clean? What happened to the nail? Where did the copper come from to cover the nail? How could this plating be used outside the classroom? Could any other metals replace copper in this activity?

The Try This Activity you just completed is called electroplating. A chemical reaction takes place in the beaker when the electric current passes through the copper sulfate solution. The copper plating on the nail comes from the solution, and as copper atoms leave the copper sulfate for the nail, they are replaced by copper atoms coming from the copper strip.

Other materials can be used for plating. Silver is sometimes used for plating metallic objects such as silverware, coffee pots, and serving trays. Gold plating is also done for inexpensive rings, pins, and watchcases. What would be the advantage of plating a metallic object rather than having the entire object made from silver or gold?

Looking at the periodic table, you'll see that the element antimony has an atomic number of 51 and is found in Group 15. Antimony is used to harden and strengthen lead, and antimony-lead alloys are used in some electrical cables. Copper, silver, and gold appear in Group 11 of the periodic table, and they are all good conductors of electricity. Most electrical wires are made with copper because it is the cheapest of these three substances.

The Periodic Table. Vertical rows—called groups—list elements with similar properties. Elements on the left side of the horizontal rows—called periods—are metals. Nonmetals are on the right side of the rows.

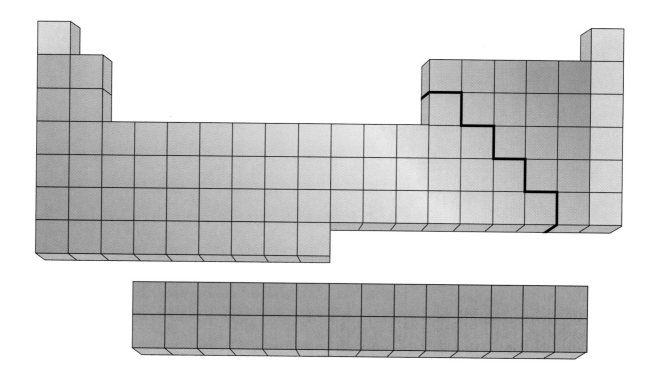

Since mercury is an element that is a liquid at normal temperatures, it is used in some thermometers and many silent electrical switches. Potassium and sodium are elements the human body needs for proper control of fluids by the cells. If your body is not receiving the proper amounts of these minerals, you may become dehydrated or develop swelling under your skin as the tissues fill with water and other fluids. What other things might depend upon the properties of potassium and sodium?

You've seen how the periodic table can be used to predict the properties of elements. You observed that elements on the left side of the table are metals that conduct electricity, and elements on the right side are nonmetals that usually don't conduct electricity.

What about the elements between metals and nonmetals? How would you group elements with some properties similar to metals and some properties similar to nonmetals? Consider silicon, for example. Silicon, with an atomic number of 14, is shiny like a metal, but it's brittle, whereas most metals bend without breaking. Since silicon is a relatively poor conductor of electricity compared to metals, we refer to it as a semiconductor. Silicon—used in the construction of computer chips and circuit boards—shares this property with arsenic and germanium.

Silicon—the second most plentiful element on Earth—is used to make transistors for radios, television sets, and computer chips.

Sum It Up

In your study of elements, you learned about the particular properties of materials that make them suitable for particular applications. Some uses have been carried forward from ancient times, such as the use of gold for making jewelry. Other uses—atom splitting to create energy for example—only became possible with relatively recent advances in technology. What predictions can you make for the use of materials beyond the year 2000? Do you think that new materials, with properties that are presently unknown, might someday be developed in a space laboratory?

In this lesson you studied systems for naming, categorizing, and displaying elements. It is interesting to note that, although the periodic table was developed more than 100 years ago, it is still flexible enough to accommodate new elements that are found. Do you think scientists will ever discover any more elements?

Using Vocabulary

families
groups
periodic table
periods

Explain the periodic table and one way it can be useful to scientists or to someone who does not know about it.

Critical Thinking

1. If an element is found on the left side of the periodic table, is it likely to conduct electricity? Why?

2. Why do some elements have symbols with more than one letter, Cu, for example?

3. How is the periodic table like a calendar?

4. Which of these elements is likely to have properties similar to chlorine? Why?
   a. bromine
   b. sulfur
   c. argon
   d. magnesium

5. Which of the above elements is most likely to have properties least like chlorine? Why?

What Are Chemical Reactions?

Chemical reactions involve nearly every aspect of life. They take place in our brains, allowing us to think. They are involved in our growth process and they can be seen in everyday examples, like burning objects and rust.

If you came to school today in an automobile, on a bus, on your bicycle, or even walked—most likely in your tennis shoes, you owe a word of thanks to American inventor Charles Goodyear. Purely by accident, Goodyear discovered a chemical reaction that improved rubber by making it less sticky, less smelly, stronger, and more springy, so that it was a better material for use in tires and shoes. Crude rubber, called India rubber, becomes brittle when cold and sticky when hot. While working in his home, Goodyear spilled a mixture of rubber and sulfur onto a hot stove. He was surprised to see that the mixture didn't melt, and he realized that heat is needed to strengthen, or cure, a rubber-sulfur mixture. Can you imagine leaving foot tracks of melted rubber behind with each step you take? Would you want to replace your bicycle tires every month because the old ones were wearing out? The formula Charles Goodyear developed more than 100 years ago for rubber eliminated many of these troublesome problems.

The manufacture of vehicle tires is the major use for synthetic rubber.

Minds On! Chemicals are everywhere. Each time you go to a grocery store, plant vegetables, ride in an automobile, or see a movie, you are surrounded by chemicals. Think about items you might find in each of these places. In your *Activity Log* on page 23, list some of the chemicals you might encounter when shopping for food, watering your garden, traveling in the car, or watching a film.●

Recall that we can identify changes in matter by observing changes in the properties of that matter. In the next activity, you will form a substance through a chemical reaction and compare its properties with the properties of the original materials.

Natural rubber is a polymer— a molecule formed by combining many smaller molecules.

Activity!

Creating a New Substance

During this activity you will investigate the results of a chemical change.

What You Need

2 250-mL beakers
water
100-mL graduated cylinder
10 mL of distilled vinegar
20 mL of chlorine bleach
small piece of fine steel wool
magnet
paper filter
tall, wide-mouthed plastic jar
rubber band
forceps
paper towels
safety goggles
***Activity Log* pages 24–25**

What To Do

1 Pour 125 mL of water into a 250-mL beaker.

2 Add 10 mL of distilled vinegar and 20 mL of chlorine bleach to the water. *Safety Tip:* Be careful not to spill the bleach or the vinegar. Wash up any spills immediately with plenty of water, and rinse any chemicals from your skin.

3 Take a piece of steel wool about 2.5 cm across in one hand and hold the magnet near. Record what happens in your ***Activity Log***.

4 Drop the steel wool into the container of water-vinegar-bleach solution. Watch what happens, and record your observations in your ***Activity Log***.

5 While the steel wool is reacting in the beaker, prepare a device for filtering. Place the coffee filter into the mouth of the wide-mouthed jar. Use the rubber band to attach the coffee filter to the top of the jar so the filter hangs into the jar.

Safety!

See the *Safety Tip* in step 2.

6 Observe the water-vinegar-bleach solution after 20 min. Then, slowly pour the steel wool and solution into the filter paper. Let the liquid drain through. Add a little water to the beaker to rinse it and pour this into the filter as well. Use forceps to pick up the steel wool, hold it over the filter, and rinse it off with a small amount of water. Then, set the steel wool aside as your teacher directs.

7 When all the water has drained through the filter, carefully remove it from the top of the jar. Place the filter on several thicknesses of paper towels. Once the material in the filter is dry, observe it carefully. Hold the magnet near the material and make a note of what happens in your *Activity Log*.

What Happened?

1. What changes occurred to the steel wool in the container? What did you notice forming on or around the steel wool?
2. What can you say about the type of material produced in the reaction?

What Now?

1. Taking into account your observation of the steel wool before, during, and the filtered material after it was in the water-vinegar-bleach solution, what do you think happened? Remember that steel wool is actually made of iron. What indicates that a chemical change occurred?
2. What do you think would happen to the steel wool in water without vinegar and chlorine bleach? Try it to see. What differences occur?

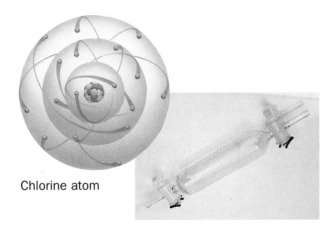

Sodium atom

Chlorine atom

The Formation of Compounds

As you saw in the previous activity, the properties of the rust—iron oxide formed when iron in the steel wool combined with oxygen—are different from the properties of the original material. The original material was attracted by a magnet, but the rust was not. The properties of compounds may be quite different from the properties of the elements that form them. **Compounds** are formed when two or more elements combine chemically. Chemically combined elements can't be separated by physical changes.

Many of the items we use each day are compounds formed by chemical reactions. Plastics, for example, are used in telephones, compact disks, and the bodies of some automobiles. Dyes color our clothes and fabrics are made from fibers. Nylon, plastic, and rubber are all compounds resulting from chemical changes during reactions.

A compound is formed by two or more elements such as sodium and chlorine, which combine to make common table salt.

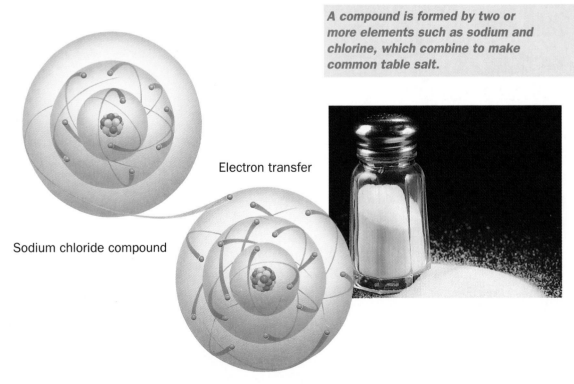

Sodium chloride compound

Electron transfer

Chemical Bonds

Compounds form during chemical reactions because of the chemical activity of the elements that are involved. In a previous lesson, you learned that electrons travel around the nucleus of atoms. Electrons have only certain energies. The amount of energy an electron has determines how far from the nucleus it can travel. On average high energy electrons travel farther from the nucleus than low energy electrons.

Atoms combine in ways that allow their outer energy levels to have a stable number of electrons—generally eight. Atoms gain, lose, or share electrons in order to have this number of electrons in their outer level.

Compounds such as lithium fluoride are formed by transferring electrons. The lithium atom has only one electron in its outer energy level—fluorine has seven. When lithium's outer electron transfers to fluorine, both atoms have stable energy levels and a new compound—lithium fluoride—is formed. When an atom gains or loses one or more electrons a charged particle, called an **ion**, is formed. One kind of bonding, or the attachment, between ions is called **ionic bonding.** Compounds with ionic bonds tend to have high melting points, well-defined crystals, do not conduct electricity, and are easily dissolved in water. Table salt, NaCl, for example is an insulator, not a conductor.

Ionic bond of lithium fluoride

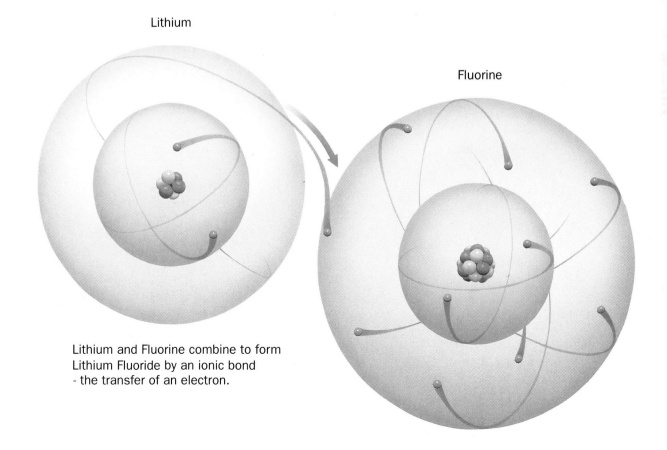

Lithium

Fluorine

Lithium and Fluorine combine to form Lithium Fluoride by an ionic bond - the transfer of an electron.

Elements can also bond in compounds by sharing—instead of transferring—electrons. **Covalent bonds** occur when one or more pairs of electrons are shared between two atoms. For example, chlorine atoms have seven electrons in their outer energy levels. They would be stable if they could get one more electron, for a total of eight. Two chlorine atoms combine by sharing one electron, giving each atom eight electrons in its outer energy level. Table sugar and ammonia are other examples of covalent compounds. Covalent compounds are brittle, don't conduct electricity, and have low melting points.

Chlorine atoms form a covalent bond by sharing electrons.

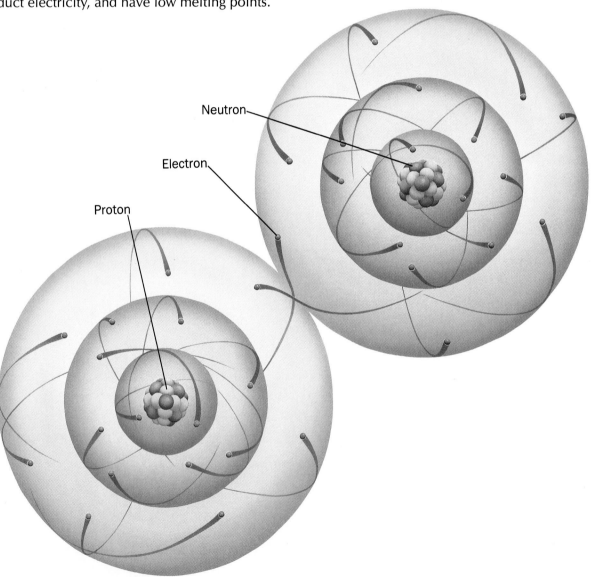

Neutron

Electron

Proton

Chemical Formulas and Equations

You may recall from Lesson 4 that elements are identified by symbols that enable scientists to discuss them easily. Similarly, chemical formulas are shorthand ways to write the names of compounds. They show us the types of elements in a chemical compound and the number of atoms that combine to form it.

As an example, you could say that hydrogen and oxygen combine to form water. But these words do not tell us how many molecules of each substance are produced. A more complete way to describe this chemical reaction is with an equation—an arrangement of numbers and symbols that shows changes that take place. The chemical equation for the formation of water is

$$2H_2 + O_2 \longrightarrow 2H_2O$$

The numbers in front of the symbols tell how much of each substance reacts or is produced.

Mass does not change in chemical reactions because matter cannot be created or destroyed. This means that the mass of the starting products in a reaction must be the same as the mass of the end products. Chemical equations must therefore be written —or balanced—to indicate that matter has not been created or destroyed. In a balanced chemical equation, the same number of each kind of atom is found on both sides of the equation. In the equation for the formation of water, four hydrogen atoms and two oxygen atoms are shown on each side of the equation, and it is balanced.

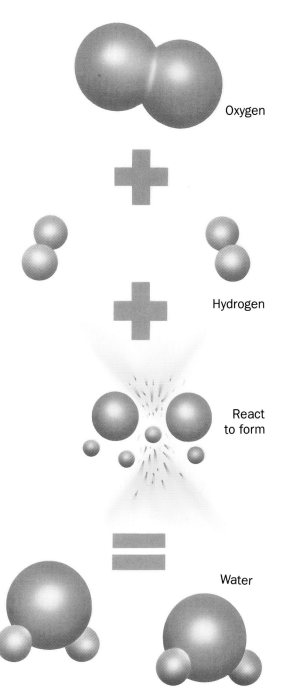

Oxygen

Hydrogen

React to form

Water

A molecule of oxygen reacts with two molecules of hydrogen to form two water molecules.

Equation for formation of water

Chemical Reactions

Although there are many chemical reactions, most of them can be classified into one of four categories. These reaction categories are synthesis, decomposition, and single and double displacement.

Synthesis Reactions

Synthesis means "putting together," or combining. In synthesis reactions, two or more elements or compounds combine to form one compound. The formation of water from hydrogen and oxygen is an example of synthesis and was given in our discussion of chemical equations. Another example is the formation of sodium chloride, table salt, from sodium and chlorine. The equation for this reaction is:

$$2Na + Cl_2 \longrightarrow 2NaCl$$

Decomposition Reactions

In decomposition reactions, we start with one substance. This one substance is broken down, or "decomposes," into one or more substances when energy is applied. For example, water can be separated into its basic elements—hydrogen and oxygen—by passing an electric current through it. The equation for this reaction—called electrolysis—is:

$$2H_2O \longrightarrow 2H_2 + O_2$$

In the next activity you can actually see a decomposition reaction working.

TRY THIS

Activity!

The Great Escape
What You Need
3 percent hydrogen peroxide (fresh), safety goggles, dropper, several cups, samples of raw foods (slice of potato, slice of mushroom), *Activity Log* page 26

Place a small slice of the foods in each cup and add a dropper of fresh hydrogen peroxide (H_2O_2). What happens? What do you think the hydrogen peroxide broke down into? In your *Activity Log,* predict whether a similar reaction would occur if you poured a small amount of fresh hydrogen peroxide on your hand? Try it and compare the result to your prediction.

In the last activity you experienced the reaction of a product breaking down into its component materials. The next type of reaction involves elements that displace other elements.

Displacement Reactions

Displacement reactions can be of two types—single and double. Displacement reactions happen when one or more elements are "displaced" or take the place of other elements. In a single displacement reaction, one element displaces another element in a compound. As an example, iron plus copper sulfate yields iron sulfate and copper. The equation for this reaction is:

$$Fe + CuSO_4 \longrightarrow FeSO_4 + Cu$$

Double-displacement reactions involve four compounds, with parts of two compounds interchanging with each other. For example, sodium hydroxide and iron chloride react to form sodium chloride and iron hydroxide. The balanced equation describing this reaction is:

$$3NaOH + FeCl_3 \longrightarrow 3NaCl + Fe(OH)_3$$

In some cases the time it takes for chemical reactions to occur is too slow to be useful. **Catalysts,** substances that increase a reaction rate without being permanently changed, may be added. Catalysts may be added to speed up the reaction time. For example, enzymes act as catalysts in the human body. Enzymes are complex proteins that act as catalysts in body cells to aid cell processes at normal body temperatures.

Automobile makers have installed devices called "catalytic converters" on vehicles. The catalytic converter gets rid of much of the harmful carbon monoxide gas or the unburned fuel by converting it into carbon dioxide. In addition, the catalytic converter works to decrease the amount of nitrogen oxides made in the car's engine. The amount of pollutants from a car's engine is significantly reduced when the catalytic converter is functioning properly. Catalytic converters have cut roughly 96 percent of the carbon monoxide out of a vehicle's exhaust and reduced nitrogen oxide emissions by 75 percent, and researchers are still looking for ways to improve the device.

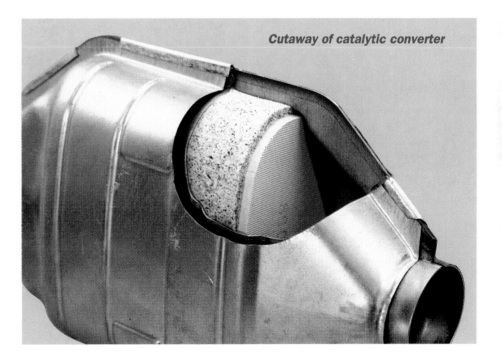

Cutaway of catalytic converter

Uses for Chemical Reactions

During all chemical reactions, there is a change in energy—energy is either released or absorbed. When wood is burned, energy in the form of heat as well as light is released. Chemical reactions that produce fireworks displays also generate heat and light.

Other chemical reactions, such as those used to prepare food, require that energy be added. This energy might come from burning wood, gas, or electric current. The energy given off by wood or coal comes from photosynthesis when the energy of sunlight forms chemical energy that is stored and later released when the substance is burned.

Energy is given off as heat and light by burning materials.

Cold packs, sometimes used to treat athletic injuries, absorb thermal energy.

More than six million chemical compounds have already been identified. Some are formed by ionic bonds and others are held together by covalent bonds. We depend on the science of chemistry and chemical interactions of various elements for a vast number of items commonly available today—from foods to medicines, or clothing materials to plastics and metals.

Minds On! How can just 109 elements combine to form more than six million compounds and all the substances that exist in the world? How is it possible to have so many combinations of elements? One way to look at it might be to take four different objects, such as a pen, a pencil, a ruler, and an eraser, and arrange them into as many different combinations as you can. How many combinations of two or more items did you get? If you vary the sequence of the objects as well, how many different combinations are there?●

The above exercise should give you some idea of the many possibilities that exist when you think of all the ways in which you could combine 109 elements. Since a compound may be composed of more than two elements, the potential for variation is even greater, and the number of possible combinations grows larger.

The English language is based on an alphabet of only 26 letters. However, look at all the words that can be made by different combinations of these 26 letters!

Focus on Technology

A Chilling Situation

The chemical reactions that form compounds have given us some remarkable materials to make our lives easier and more comfortable, but they've also created problems for the world's environment. For example, chlorofluorocarbons (klôr ō flôr′ ə kär′ bənz) (CFCs) are compounds used to make refrigerators, insulators, and cleaning agents for sophisticated electronic equipment. CFCs were first invented in the 1930s by combining atoms of the elements carbon, chlorine, fluorine, and hydrogen. Scientists immediately found many uses for CFCs, but their hazards have only recently become known.

When CFCs work their way into the atmosphere, they may form compounds that aid in depleting Earth's protective ozone layer. This layer shields us from receiving too many harmful ultraviolet rays from the sun. This erosion of the planet's ozone layer is particularly noticeable at the Arctic and Antarctic poles. It is so serious that in 1989 representatives of 81 nations met in Helsinki, Finland, to approve a total ban on CFC production by 1999. In the meantime, scientists are searching for alternatives to CFCs. One fast-food producer required its packaging suppliers to eliminate CFCs in the manufacturing of polystyrene foam packaging.

Researchers in the refrigeration industry may also have found one answer to the problems of CFCs by updating a 19th-century engine with modern technology. The new device is called a "cryonic cooler," and it is based on an engine design that Scottish clergyman and inventor Robert Stirling developed in 1816.

Stirling's engine worked by applying heat to one end of a cylinder filled with helium gas. The expanding gas would move a piston to the other end of the cylinder, producing mechanical power. The original Stirling engine was soon replaced by the internal combustion engine, yet the concept remains potentially useful because of its ability to get the helium gas within the cylinder to absorb heat, instead of releasing heat.

The Upper Atmosphere Research Satellite, launched from Discovery will enable scientists to study ozone depletion in Earth's upper atmosphere.

Sum It Up

You have seen that chemical reactions are all around us and are even essential to life. These reactions are the result of interactions between substances where matter is only altered, not lost or gained.

How does this affect you? Some chemical reactions such as the ammonia-based fertilizers that put nitrogen into the soil have beneficial effects. Others—the rusting of metal, or the breakdown of Earth's protective ozone layer from the release of chlorofluorocarbons into the air—have negative impacts. If we understand how and why chemical reactions occur, we can use them to our best advantage.

Using Vocabulary

catalysts
compounds
covalent bonds
ionic bonding
ions

Indicate whether the following statements are true or false on a separate sheet of paper. If the statement is false, correct it using one of the vocabulary words from this lesson.
1. Charged particles from atoms that have gained or lost electrons are called ions.

2. Catalysts speed up reactions without being changed themselves.
3. Ionic bonds between atoms are produced by the sharing of electrons.
4. In ionic matching, ions are held together by the attraction of their opposite charges.
5. The composition of compounds is always the same.

Critical Thinking

1. Compare and contrast ionic and covalent compounds.

2. You know that symbols are used for elements. Explain what a chemical formula is and what it means to have a balanced equation.

3. There are four main categories of reactions. Describe in words what takes place in each type of reaction.

4. When does an atom become stable?

5. Millions of compounds are known. Do you think it is possible for new compounds to be developed? Explain and discuss some of the benefits and risks of developing new compounds.

Chemical Compounds

The recipe for a chocolate cake calls for a tablespoon of baking soda. Without this ingredient, the cake will look flat like a brownie, not tall and light. A baker who makes this cake uses chemistry—knowledge of the behavior of specific compounds. How do scientists use chemicals? How can they predict the behavior of specific chemicals? In this lesson you will enter the world of the chemist and discover some major chemical families and how to identify them.

You have probably heard the terms *acids* and *bases*. In your **Activity Log** on page 27, write down what you think acids and bases are. List several examples of each.

Have you ever added vinegar to baking soda? The bubbles that form when the vinegar and baking soda react are a gas. If you drop a piece of chalk into a container of vinegar, bubbles of the same gas form. Vinegar is a dilute form of acetic acid. Baking soda and chalk are both compounds called carbonates—sodium bicarbonate and calcium carbonate. Acids always react with carbonates, producing a gas called carbon dioxide.

Acids and bases—two important chemical groups that are the components of many common materials—react in predictable and identifiable ways. The specific ways compounds behave are called properties and can be used as indicators to distinguish between groups of compounds. The following Explore Activity will give you an opportunity to examine properties of some common materials.

Acids and bases are found in many consumer products, such as yogurt, vinegar, citrus fruits, ammonia cleaners, milk of magnesia, and deodorants.

Activity!

Acids and Bases

In this activity, you will observe some of the properties of common materials that are either acidic or basic.

What You Need

red and blue litmus paper
wide-range indicator paper
small test tube
droppers
paper towels
goggles
apron
household solutions (ammonia cleaning solution, antacid liquid, bleach, carbonated beverage, powdered detergent solution, lemon juice, milk, cold tea, vinegar)
Activity Log pages 28–29

What To Do

1 Lay one strip each of red and blue litmus paper and wide-range indicator paper on a paper towel. *Safety Tip:* Put on your safety goggles and apron. Place 1 drop of vinegar on each of the strips. Observe the colors and note them in your *Activity Log*. Also, record the pH shown by the color of the wide-range indicator paper. (The pH scale is a method of measuring acid or base strength.) Dispose of all materials as your teacher directs.

2 Repeat step 1 with the other solutions. Note the results in your *Activity Log*.

Safety!

See the *Safety Tip* in step 1.

3 Add 20 drops of detergent solution to a small test tube. Now, put 10 drops of vinegar into the same test tube, a drop at a time. Covering the top of the test tube with your finger, shake the test tube to mix the solutions thoroughly. Make a note of any changes you may observe in your *Activity Log*.

4 Test a drop of the resulting solution with a strip of wide-range indicator paper. Record the pH value of it in your *Activity Log*.

What Happened?

1. Detergent is a base. Vinegar is an acid. Compared to these two materials, which other substances that you tested were acids and which ones were bases?
2. Look at the pH values in your table. Which values indicate an acid and which values indicate a base? Which number seems to be the neutral point?
3. What was the pH of the solution that came from mixing the detergent with vinegar in steps 3 and 4?

What Now?

1. Do you think all acids or all bases have the same pH value?
2. What do all the nonfood items have in common? *Caution:* Never taste a solution to see if it is an acid or a base.

EXPLORE

Chemical Compounds

All matter is made of elements, compounds, or mixtures. In Lesson 4, you studied elements—substances that can't be broken down into other substances. In Lesson 7 you will learn about mixtures.

This lesson focuses on compounds—substances formed when two or more elements combine chemically. Compounds are important to us because elements usually are not used by themselves. When types of compounds have common properties, scientists classify them into groups, such as acids and bases. In discussing acids and bases, it is useful to have a standard way to identify and measure their properties.

Measurement of Acidity

In the Explore Activity, you used wide-range indicator paper to measure the pH of acids and bases. The pH value of a substance indicates the concentration of an acid or base in a water solution. The pH scale runs from 0 to 14. A pH reading of 7 indicates that a solution is neutral (neither an acid nor a base). A pH value of less than 7 means that the solution is acidic, while a pH higher than 7 shows that a solution is basic.

The wide-range indicator paper turned different colors, each associated with an approximate pH value, while the litmus paper only turned red or blue to reveal whether a substance had the properties of an acid or a base.

Hydrangea plants—natural indicators—develop pink flowers when grown in basic soils and blue flowers in acidic soils.

Compounds identified as acids are produced within our bodies and are essential to life. Many acids are found in foods and other common substances. Others have important industrial uses.

ACIDS

Acids are compounds that release hydrogen ions when dissolved in water. These hydrogen ions are attracted to water molecules and form hydronium ions. Acids taste sour—although tasting is not a safe way to test for either acids or bases—and turn blue litmus paper red as you noticed in the Explore Activity. Red litmus paper remains red when tested with an acid.

Some acids are identified as weak and others as strong. Strong acids have greater concentrations of hydronium ions than weak acids. Weak acids are found in tomatoes, pickles, and citrus fruits. Strong acids, such as sulfuric, nitric, and hydrochloric, are used in science laboratories and industry. Table 1 lists some common acids and their uses.

In the following Try This Activity, you can try your hand at using a simple test for acids and bases.

TRY THIS

Boil That Cabbage Down

You've learned that tasting a substance is not a safe way to determine whether it is an acid or a base. Try the red cabbage juice test instead. Red cabbage juice, like litmus paper, can be used as an acid/base indicator.

What You Need
red cabbage juice
3 cups
dropper
3 craft sticks
lemon juice, vinegar, baking powder, tea, shampoo, fruit juice
Activity Log page 30

1. Place a small amount of vinegar, lemon juice, and baking powder in separate cups.
2. Add 5 drops of the cabbage juice to each cup and stir the mixtures. Observe what happens and record your observations in the *Activity Log*.

What color did the cabbage juice turn in the vinegar and lemon juice? Did the cabbage juice turn a different color in the baking powder? Which substances do you think are acids and which are bases? Explain your reasoning.

Predict what would happen if you tested other common substances such as tea, shampoo, or fruit juice, and record your predictions in the *Activity Log*. Perform the tests and compare your results with your predictions. Were there any surprises?

TABLE 1: Common Acids

Name	Formula	Common Occurrence
Acetic	CH_3COOH	vinegar
Boric	H_3BO_3	eye drops
Carbonic	H_2CO_3	carbonated beverages, also produced in body when carbon dioxide dissolves in blood
Citric	$C_6H_8O_7$	citrus fruits (limes, lemons, oranges, etc.)
Hydrochloric	HCl	stomach acids, industrial and home cleaning agents
Lactic	$C_6H_6O_3$	sour milk, yogurt, also produced in the muscles during contraction
Nitric	HNO_3	manufacturing agent in dyes and explosives, also used in urine test for protein
Phosphoric	H_3PO_4	cola soft drinks, also used in the making of fertilizers
Sulfuric	H_2SO_4	automobile batteries, also used in the manufacturing of fertilizers and other items

BASES

Bases produce hydroxyl ions—an ion of oxygen and hydrogen—in water solutions. The fewer hydroxyl ions, the weaker the base. Strong bases, with more hydroxyl ions, react with human and animal substances and must be handled very carefully.

Although they should not be tasted or touched to identify them, bases taste bitter and feel slippery. They turn red litmus blue. Blue litmus paper remains blue in the presence of a base. Bases are used in homes for cleaning floors, bathtubs, and drains. Table 2 lists some bases and their uses.

TABLE 2: Common Bases

Name	Formula	Common Occurrence
Aluminum Hydroxide	$Al(OH)_3$	Antacid, Deodorant
Sodium Hydroxide	NaOH	Oven Cleaner, Drain Cleaner
Magnesium Hydroxide	$Mg(OH)_2$	Milk of Magnesia (Antacid)
Ammonia	NH_3	Household Cleaner
Calcium Hydroxide	$Ca(OH)_2$	Used in the making of plaster and mortar

Neutralization and Salts

When an acid reacts with a base, a chemical change called neutralization takes place. **Neutralization** is a process in which hydronium ions from an acid combine with hydroxide ions from a base to form water and a salt in a double-replacement reaction. As an example, hydrochloric acid and sodium hydroxide react to form water and sodium chloride.

$$HCl + NaOH \longrightarrow H_2O + NaCl$$

Salt is a general term for the product formed in the neutralization reaction between an acid and a base. Salt is also the common name for table salt—sodium chloride. We often use salts in everyday life—sodium bicarbonate ($NaHCO_3$) is commonly called baking soda, calcium carbonate ($CaCO_3$) is chalk and limestone, and potassium chloride (KCl) serves as a salt substitute for people on a low-sodium diet.

Paper's ingredients can slowly react with water vapor to form a low concentration of sulfuric acid, which causes pages to crumble. Important documents, such as Yale University's Historical Book collection, can be preserved with special neutralizing treatments.

Health Link
Helping Heartburn

Bases are often used in over-the-counter medicines marketed to consumers for the temporary relief of indigestion or heartburn. Conduct library research on these types of products. Write a report on the compounds used in these products and whether or not they seem to be effective.

Oxides Everywhere

Oxides are another group of compounds containing oxygen and one other element. If the other element is a metal, the compounds formed are called metallic oxides. If the second element is a nonmetal, the compounds are identified as nonmetallic oxides. Generally, metal oxides form basic solutions and nonmetal oxides make acidic solutions when they dissolve in water.

Many oxygen compounds have beneficial uses. For example water—H_2O—is necessary for life. Hydrogen peroxide—H_2O_2—is used to kill germs and as a bleach.

Acid rain, a nonmetallic oxide has caused erosion of this statue.

Unfortunately, not all oxide compounds have positive effects. Sometimes they create problems that must be resolved. When we travel by bus or car, several nonmetallic oxides, including carbon dioxide, are produced in a gaseous state. In the atmosphere, carbon dioxide combines with water vapor to produce a weak carbonic acid. In nature, naturally occurring carbonic acid creates interesting looking stalactites and stalagmites in caves when it reacts with the calcium carbonate of underground limestone. But the acids formed from nitrogen oxide and water or carbon dioxide and water corrode stone buildings and artworks.

SCIENCE TECHNOLOGY AND Society **Focus on Environment**

Obnoxious Oxides

When gasoline and other petroleum products are burned in automobiles and factories, hydrocarbons and nitrogen oxides are released into the air. Sunlight reacts with these combustion products, forming smog—a type of air pollution. Local weather conditions sometimes prevent smog from lifting and dispersing, and mountain ranges around cities can trap smog.

Smog can irritate the eyes, nose, and throat and damage the lungs. In heavy concentrations it can be dangerous to persons who already have difficulty breathing.

Smog can also create visibility problems. Although a person might be able to see as far as 150 miles under ideal natural conditions, in Denver the average visibility is just 20 miles. Visibility in Los Angeles is often only eight miles.

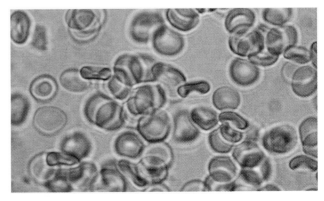

The word smog—a type of air pollution that hangs over cities—is derived from the words smoke and fog.

Organic and Inorganic Compounds

Organic chemistry is the study of carbon compounds. Carbon compounds are important because about 80 percent of all known compounds contain carbon. Millions of other organic compounds have also been made in laboratories because carbon atoms readily bond with other carbon atoms or with atoms of other elements. One of the most important groups of carbon compounds is called hydrocarbons. Hydrocarbons contain only carbon and hydrogen and produce carbon dioxide and water when they burn. Most usable hydrocarbons come from coal, natural gas, and petroleum. Hydrocarbons with few carbon atoms are used primarily for fuels and solvents, and those with more carbon atoms for greases and lubricants. Synthetic fibers such as nylon and rayon, synthetic rubber, and plastics are all produced from petroleum, a liquid mixture of hydrocarbons found below Earth's surface.

The study of chemical elements and their compounds, except for most carbon compounds, is called **inorganic chemistry.** Oxygen, nitrogen, and boron, among others—important nonmetallic elements—can combine to form inorganic compounds. So are groups—coordinating compounds—in which a metal atom is surrounded by atoms of nonmetals. Hemoglobin, for example, a substance in blood that carries oxygen, contains atoms of iron combined with atoms of nitrogen and oxygen.

Hemoglobin, an organic compound in red blood cells, gives blood its red color.

Scientists who understand the composition and behavior of compounds can provide many useful services to society. In this career example, you will see how chemicals can help convict criminals.

How Forensic Chemists Help Secure Justice

Chemists are interested in—among many other things—the analysis of compounds into their component elements and the reactions of elements and compounds. Perhaps no one knows this better than those involved in criminal justice systems—both the enforcers and those accused.

Forensic chemists examine samples of paint, paper, hair, fabric, blood, or other materials that could be used as evidence in solving a crime. *Forensic* comes from a Latin word meaning "court of law."

Forensic chemists carefully investigate crime evidence.

Suppose that during a burglary, the criminal cut himself or herself and left a small amount of blood either on a broken window or even as a small drop on the carpeting. When the police examine the scene of the crime, they painstakingly cover the area searching for clues, and in their search they discover the bloodstain. If the police have a suspect, they could verify that the blood actually belonged to the suspect.

This could be done initially by blood typing and identifying whether the blood could be the suspect's. If the sample were verified as a possible match with the suspect, further testing could confirm whether it belonged to the suspect.

The further testing is called "fingerprinting" of hereditary material. Genetic fingerprinting was developed by geneticist Alec Jeffreys at the University of Leicester in Great Britain. While searching for genetic differences that might indicate a tendency for a person to have an inherited disease, Jeffreys realized that the same differences in genetic material could accurately identify an individual, because no two people, except identical twins, have identical genetic material.

Genetic fingerprinting is so precise that it can be a key to the identity of a person who was at the crime scene. Previously, most efforts

to identify the source of biological evidence was limited to the work of serologists. Serologists study the preparation, use, and properties of serums, blood, and other body fluids. They could, by studying these fluids, narrow a list of suspects, suggest that a person might be guilty, or prove that someone was innocent. But they couldn't prove conclusively who was at the scene of the crime.

Given the burglary example, a small blood sample from the crime scene would be collected along with a small sample of the suspect's blood. Chemists would break down the genetic strands of the cells in the two blood samples. By comparing the two strands, an identification could be made if the strands matched. This evidence would then be presented in court.

People who are interested in possible careers as forensic chemists might have aptitudes and interests in science and mathematics and plan to attend universities that offer specialized training. For information on a career as a forensic chemist, write to:

American Academy of Forensic Science
P. O. Box 669
Colorado Springs, Colorado 80904-0669

Sum It Up

As you have seen throughout this lesson, there are many chemical compounds, and they interact with each other in different and interesting ways. You're able to use their properties to classify them. These organic and inorganic chemical compounds have a number of uses that are beneficial to society. However, their use may produce harmful side effects as well. The more we know about the properties of chemical compounds, the better we can devise methods of using them and reducing, or eliminating, the problems they create.

Using Vocabulary

acids	**neutralization**
bases	**organic chemistry**
inorganic chemistry	**salt**

Write a short story about a master detective solving a crime. Use at least four of the vocabulary words in this lesson in your story.

Critical Thinking

1. If you were given an unknown liquid, how could you determine if it was an acid or a base?

2. What would you suspect if the pH of the unknown liquid was 4? What if it was 7?

3. Imagine that you have some vinegar with a little red cabbage juice added. The pH is 3. Now imagine that you add baking soda until the color changes from pink to green. What do you think the pH would be now?

4. Which would be a better home remedy for an acid stomach, a little vinegar in water or a little baking soda in water? Why?

5. What is the result when equal strengths and amounts of an acid and a base are combined?

Mixtures

Think about filling a large bowl with glass and steel marbles. After you have poured them all into the bowl, you decide you want to arrange them in a different way. How can you use the properties of each item to help you separate them back into two groups?

Minds On! Imagine you are in a kitchen with apples, pears, bananas, and oranges on the counter in front of you. After peeling the skins, you begin to slice each fruit, noticing the colors, the smell, and feel of the pieces. When all the fruit is sliced, you put it into a bowl and gently stir the pieces together, making a fruit salad for dinner.

Do the pieces of fruit in the fruit salad have different properties than the original

fruits? On page 31 of your *Activity Log*, write a plan to separate out only the apple or pear pieces.●

There are other combinations of matter besides marbles and fruit that you might encounter on a day-to-day basis. Salt water is one. Ink is another. In the Explore Activity, think about the combinations and properties of the marbles and fruits as you investigate an ink sample.

The oceans—combinations of salt, solids, and water—cover about 70 percent of Earth's surface.

Salts 3.5%

Sodium Chloride
Magnesium Chloride
Magnesium Sulfate
Calcium Sulfate
Potassium Sulfate
Calcium Carbonate
Magnesium Bromide

Water 96.5%

Activity!

What You See May Not Be What You Get

Through investigating ink samples, you can observe how some combinations of matter can be separated, by physical methods, into its different components.

What You Need

filter paper
metric ruler
paper towels
washable color markers
pencil
tape
tall, wide-mouthed jar
water
Activity Log pages 32–33

What To Do

1 Measure and cut several strips of filter paper 12 cm long. Lay them on a clean paper towel, and use your pencil to draw a line 2 cm from the bottom of the paper strips.

2 Using yellow, blue, green, and black markers, put a dot of each color every 2 cm along the pencil line.

3 Place 1 cm of water in a tall, wide-mouthed jar. The water level must be below the level of the colored dots on the paper.

4 Next fasten the filter paper strips to the inside of the jar with tape, with the dots toward the bottom and let the water rise up the paper until it's roughly 1 cm from the top.

5 Remove the paper strips from the jar and lay them on a paper towel to dry. Look at the filter paper. What do you see? In your *Activity Log,* record your observations of any changes in the appearance of the colored dots or of the paper itself.

What Happened?

1. What happened as the water moved up the paper through the ink dots?
2. Describe the differences you observed in the different colors of ink. What changed?

What Now?

1. If a student from another class showed you filter paper results from several unknown materials, could you identify a sample of black ink? In your *Activity Log,* explain why you would or wouldn't be able to recognize it.
2. Can you infer that all washable black inks would produce the same pattern? Why or why not? Try it and see. Repeat the activity using a different brand of washable marker.

EXPLORE

Mixtures of Matter

Recall that in the Explore Activity the black ink was actually a mixture of different colors that you separated by physical means.

What exactly is a mixture? A **mixture** is formed when two or more substances combine without a chemical change occurring. Mixtures have the same properties as the materials they were made of, and they do not have a definite amount of each material in the mixture. Compounds, as you may recall, are two or more elements chemically combined, having properties different than their original materials. Mixtures can be made by combining elements, compounds, or compounds and elements.

Mixtures are everywhere around us—in fact, mixtures are the most common form of matter. Salt water is a mixture. So are many fabrics. Brass is an alloy (metal mixture) of copper and zinc. Can you think of any other mixtures? What about a cup of coffee with cream and sugar in it? Cream is a mixture containing calcium, fat compounds, water, and other compounds. Sugar is a compound, yet when cream and sugar are added to coffee, you create a mixture.

German silver alloy—a combination of copper, zinc, and nickel—is used for jewelry and silver plating.

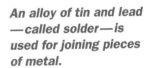

An alloy of tin and lead —called solder—is used for joining pieces of metal.

Wrought iron—an alloy of iron, copper, and manganese—is used in the manufacture of railings and sculptures.

A fresh salad is a heteroge-neous mixture. The salad dressing is a suspension.

Mixtures have variable compositions. They can be divided into two groups—homogeneous (hō′ mə jē′nē əs) mixtures and heterogeneous (het′ər ə jē′nē əs) mixtures.

Homogeneous Mixtures

Homogeneous mixtures—also called solutions—have ingredients that are evenly spread throughout the mixture. Particles in a solution do not settle out but can be separated by physical methods, such as filtering, using a magnet, dissolving in water, or evaporation. Solutions form when a material—the solute—dissolves in another material—the solvent. Water is the most common solvent in solutions. How many solutions exist right around you and in your school? Did you think of carbonated beverages, vinegar, or mothballs?

Mixtures can be found in all states of matter. Air is a mixture of gases. Tap water consists of dissolved minerals and gases in the air. Fruit juices, coffee, and tea contain a number of different solids dissolved in water. The alloy that dentists use to make fillings for your teeth is a solution composed of solid and liquid metals. **Alloys** are mixtures of two or more metallic elements.

Can you think of methods to separate the different materials in a mixture? So far we've focused mostly on properties of a suspended substance. What about properties of a solvent? Would you be able to separate the solids from the liquids in a solution by changing the state of matter of the solution? The Try This Activity on the next page will investigate evaporation as a separation process.

Heterogeneous Mixtures

In a **heterogeneous mixture,** components are unevenly spread throughout the mixture and sometimes can be seen clearly. A drawer full of loose socks, soil, a pizza, or concrete are examples of heterogeneous mixtures.

Heterogeneous mixtures can take the form of suspensions. In **suspensions,** solid or liquid particles of matter are suspended in a gas or liquid. The suspended substances will separate—gravity will draw the heavier components to the bottom of a container if left undisturbed. Italian salad dressing is a suspension of spices in a mixture of liquid that will separate into the spices, vinegar, and oil. Dust in the air is a type of suspension, as is sediment in muddy water.

Activity!

Water + Salt + Heat = ?

Some mixtures separate when they are left undisturbed. You have already seen how to separate the components of a mixture with filter paper in the Explore Activity, but are there other ways to separate the "parts" of a mixture? Let's see what happens if we use evaporation.

What You Need

water, salt, measuring cup, spoon, heat source, aluminum tray, thermal mitt, *Activity Log* page 34

Stir 2 spoonfuls of salt into 1/2 cup of water to prepare a salt solution. Keep stirring until the salt has completely dissolved in the water and none of it is visible. Pour a little of the salt water into the aluminum tray. In your *Activity Log,* predict what will happen when the water evaporates.

Put the aluminum tray on a heat source. Heat the solution until all the water has evaporated. *Safety Tip:* Be sure to stay close to the equipment. Do not let the aluminum tray become too hot.

Answer the following questions in your *Activity Log.* What remains in the tray? Where is the water now? How did converting the water from a liquid to a gas change the solution?

Colloids

Solutions and suspensions are two kinds of mixtures, but there is also a third type of mixture called a colloid. **Colloids** are mixtures containing particles that stay mixed in another substance. Colloid particle sizes are between those of a solution and a suspension. As with solutions, the particles of a colloid appear to be spread evenly throughout the substance. These particles don't settle out like those in suspensions; however, they do pass through ordinary filter paper in the same way that particles in a solution do.

Colloid particles are large enough that they scatter a beam of light. This **Tyndall effect** —named after British scientist John Tyndall, who discovered the effect—can be observed when a sunbeam comes through a hole in blinds or when automobile headlights are seen in the fog.

Many substances in everyday life are colloids. The next Try This Activity will let you try your hand at creating a common colloid.

Sunbeams are sometimes visible because dust and water particles in the air scatter light —a property of colloids.

Activity!

Creating a Colloid

What You Need
small jar with lid
1/2 pt of heavy cream
clean marble
Activity Log page 35

Fill a small jar with 1/2 pt of heavy cream. Carefully add a clean marble. Screw the lid onto the jar tightly so you're sure it won't leak. Shake the jar moderately back and forth and in an up-and-down, figure-eight, motion. Continue shaking the jar until you get a rapid change in the sound of the marble or the consistency of the contents.

Predict in your *Activity Log* what you will find inside the jar.

In the activity you just completed, you created a colloid from a liquid. Colloids also come in other combinations. A liquid in a liquid—milk for example—is called an emulsion. Liquids or solids dispersed in gases—like fog or smog—are called aerosols, and a gas dispersed in a liquid or solid—such as whipped cream or marshmallow—is termed a foam.

Milk, fog, marshmallows, and whipped cream—all colloids—contain undissolved particles or droplets that stay mixed in another substance.

Mighty Mixtures

Blood

Perhaps no chemical mixture is as important to us as our blood. Composed mainly of water, blood contains many other compounds and elements that are essential to our health—such as salt, sodium, potassium, calcium, and iron. Since blood is the chemical mixture around which the whole circulatory system operates, it affects every other system in the body.

Blood is unique in that it's a solution, a suspension, and a colloid. It consists of tiny specks of matter that form red blood cells, white blood cells, and platelets.

Rocks

You may not have thought of rocks as mixtures, but they are combinations of one or more minerals. Of more than 3,000 different minerals, only about a dozen form rocks. The most common mineral-forming chemicals are silicates, carbonates, oxides, sulfates, and halides. Igneous rocks—rock mixtures formed from magma—comprise about 95 percent of Earth's crust.

Fabrics

Fabrics can be mixtures of materials such as cotton and polyester. Bed sheets, for example, might contain a 50 percent blend of cotton and polyester fibers. The properties of the fabric are a combination of the properties of the cotton and polyester. Cotton is easily dyed and is absorbent. Polyesters—chemically bonded compounds—resist wrinkles and shrinkage.

Alloys

Alloys are mixtures that contain more than one element and have metallic properties. The use of alloys dates back as far as 3000 B.C. when it was discovered in Mesopotamia, that bronze—a combination of copper and tin—was a durable product. As another example, gold is mixed with copper and silver to form a harder material for use in jewelry. Pure gold is said to be 24 karat, so a 12-karat item contains 50 percent gold. Gold coins, containing 92 percent gold, are 22 karat.

This bronze stand was discovered on the island of Cyprus. Cyprus was a major source of copper for traders in the bronze age.

Sum It Up

Mixtures are the most common form of matter on Earth. The way matter interacts and combines has a direct impact on your life in countless ways. For example, if you need fillings for your teeth or wear any kind of jewelry, the odds are that the fillings or jewelry consist of an alloy. If you drink milk, you are consuming an emulsion.

The chemical and physical properties of matter and its interactions are also at work when a giant tanker leaks an oil spill at sea and the crude oil washes up on the beach. In response to this environmental problem, scientists continue to research materials to change the chemical properties of the oil, allowing it to mix with water.

Mixtures abound in our world. From the dust we see in the air to the fruit we find in raspberry gelatin, there is no escaping the matter of mixtures and the mixtures of matter.

Using Vocabulary

alloys
colloids
heterogeneous mixture
homogeneous mixtures
mixture
suspensions
Tyndall effect

Write a sentence, describing in your own words, each of the vocabulary words in this lesson.

Critical Thinking

1. How are mixtures different from compounds?

2. How would you separate a mixture of sugar and water?

3. Give an example of a mixture made up of a:
   a. solid in a liquid
   b. solid in a gas
   c. solid in a solid
   d. liquid in a gas
   e. gas in a liquid
   f. gas in a gas

4. How are heterogeneous mixtures different from homogeneous mixtures? Give an example of each.

5. How would you separate a mixture of water, salt, iron filings, and sand?

Matter *Does* Matter

The opening pages of this unit set the stage for your study of matter by indicating how fundamental and important matter is in the universe. Everything we feel, hear, see, smell, and taste exists because of matter. Our knowledge of the world around us depends largely on our knowledge of matter, its structure, and how different types of matter interact with each other. By identifying the properties that exist in a particular type of matter, we can determine how to use it to our best advantage —as a building material, a fuel, a piece of jewelry, a food additive, or for any number of other things, from clothing fibers to the outside surface of a jet aircraft. By knowing the struc-

ture of matter, we can figure out how to take it apart and put it back together again. This allows us to make new materials with new properties and new uses.

In the unit we discussed many different ways to classify matter—by its state (solid, liquid, or gas)—by its elements on the periodic table—by the compounds it is composed of—and by how it exists as a heterogeneous or homogeneous mixture.

Veil Nebula, photographed at the Palomar Observatory in California, is probably the result of a supernova explosion in prehistoric times.

We have seen how the characteristics of matter determine the use of an object and the selection of certain compounds and elements for specific purposes. We studied the chemical properties of matter, too, and this taught us that the way a substance reacts—or fails to react—with another substance can also determine its use. We know that whether or not a substance burns when mixed with one or more other substances is an important consideration in deciding how and where to make different types of matter work for us. We learned the meaning of a pH value, and how that property may affect a material's purpose as well. Knowing these facts about the physical and chemical properties of matter, you wouldn't try to build a canoe out of butter any more than you would drink a glass of lemon juice to soothe an upset stomach.

A scanning transmission electron microscope photograph of microcrystals. Each spot represents an atom.

Yet, it's not enough just to be able to recite the physical and chemical properties of matter. We must understand how and why those properties exist the way they do in different kinds of materials. For this reason we studied the atomic structure of the elements and analyzed atoms and molecules to see how many protons, neutrons, and electrons they possess, or what electric charge they carry. This knowledge helps us determine the way atoms of various elements are either attracted to or repelled from each other. With this knowledge we can explain why a compound of two or more elements has chemical and physical properties that none of the elements would possess alone.

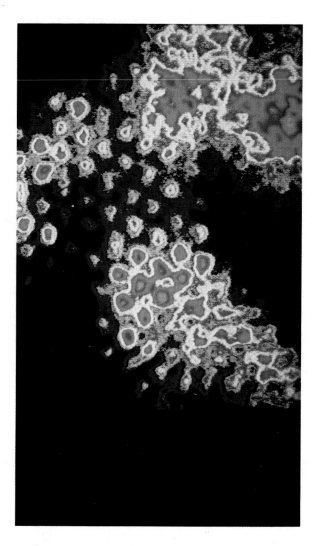

All life on Earth depends on chemical reactions. And all chemical reactions are caused by the interactions of matter. Without atoms of oxygen and nitrogen, you wouldn't have air to breathe. Without carbon atoms, there would be no animals to breathe air and produce the carbon dioxide that plants need to maintain the chemical reaction of photosynthesis, which keeps them alive, so they can release oxygen.

You know how to classify matter, and you've learned what forms different elements can take, and how the various structures of the atoms in those elements determine the way that one type of matter interacts with another type of matter. These classifications relate to the scale and structure of matter, as well as to the systems and interactions it may involve.

Carbon compounds are found in all living things, as well as in foods and fuels.

Diamonds are a hard form of carbon formed by a network of carbon atoms.

Graphite, a soft form of carbon, is soft and slippery. It is formed by carbon atoms arranged in layers.

Paraffin, another carbon compound, is used in candle making.

Minds On! So far you have studied matter as it exists—with familiar forms, familiar properties, and in a familiar environment. Do you think matter and its properties might change in a more unusual environment, such as in the zero gravity of outer space? Picture yourself as a scientist in an orbiting laboratory. Imagine what you could do to develop new materials, or encourage new properties and uses in existing substances. How would you expect mixtures to act in a weightless environment? What experiments would you conduct? How might a space station laboratory improve research into biomedical and engineering applications of technology? In your **Activity Log** on page 36, write a brief television news bulletin describing an imaginary scientific breakthrough you have just made. Perhaps you can share your idea with your classmates—taking turns and reading them aloud.●

Scientists in orbiting space laboratories can conduct experiments in producing biological materials, medicine, and astronomy.

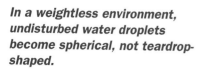

In a weightless environment, undisturbed water droplets become spherical, not teardrop-shaped.

GLOSSARY

Use the pronunciation key below to help you decode, or read, the pronunciations.

Pronunciation Key

a	at, bad	d	dear, soda, bad
ā	ape, pain, day, break	f	five, defend, leaf, off, cough, elephant
ä	father, car, heart	g	game, ago, fog, egg
âr	care, pair, bear, their, where	h	hat, ahead
e	end, pet, said, heaven, friend	hw	white, whether, which
ē	equal, me, feet, team, piece, key	j	joke, enjoy, gem, page, edge
i	it, big, English, hymn	k	kite, bakery, seek, tack, cat
ī	ice, fine, lie, my	l	lid, sailor, feel, ball, allow
îr	ear, deer, here, pierce	m	man, family, dream
o	odd, hot, watch	n	not, final, pan, knife
ō	old, oat, toe, low	ng	long, singer, pink
ô	coffee, all, taught, law, fought	p	pail, repair, soap, happy
ôr	order, fork, horse, story, pour	r	ride, parent, wear, more, marry
oi	oil, toy	s	sit, aside, pets, cent, pass
ou	out, now	sh	shoe, washer, fish mission, nation
u	up, mud, love, double	t	tag, pretend, fat, button, dressed
ū	use, mule, cue, feud, few	th	thin, panther, both
ü	rule, true, food	th	this, mother, smooth
u̇	put, wood, should	v	very, favor, wave
ûr	burn, hurry, term, bird, word, courage	w	wet, weather, reward
ə	about, taken, pencil, lemon, circus	y	yes, onion
b	bat, above, job	z	zoo, lazy, jazz, rose, dogs, houses
ch	chin, such, match	zh	vision, treasure, seizure

acids (as′ idz) substances that dissolve in water to produce hydronium ions; chemical compounds that can be neutralized by a base; substances that have a pH below 7

alloys mixtures of two or more metallic elements

atomic number the number of protons in the nucleus of an atom

bases (bās əz) substances that increase the hydroxide ion concentration when added to water; chemical compounds that can be neutralized by an acid; substances having a pH above 7

catalysts substances that speed up or slow down chemical reactions while remaining chemically unchanged themselves

chemical change a change in which a substance becomes another substance having different properties

chemical property characteristics of a substance that determine how a substance reacts to form other substances

colloids (kol′ oidz) non-separating mixtures with a particle size between that of solutions and suspensions

compound a substance containing atoms of two or more elements chemically combined, always in the same ratio

covalent bonds (kō vā′ lənt) bonds between atoms produced by the sharing of electrons

density (den′ si tē) the mass of material divided by its volume; expressed as g/cm^3

electrons (i lek' tron) a negatively charged particle that moves around the nucleus of an atom

element substance that cannot be broken down by physical or chemical means; composed of one kind of atom

families a group of elements with common characteristics or properties

groups a vertical column in the periodic table listing elements having similar chemical properties

heterogeneous mixture a mixture where components are unevenly spaced throughout and sometimes can be seen easily

homogeneous mixtures solutions that have ingredients evenly spaced throughout

indicators (in' di kā' tarz) organic compounds that change color in an acid or a base

inorganic chemistry the study of chemical elements and their compounds, except for most carbon compounds

inorganic compound (in' ôr gan' ik) in general, any compound not containing carbon

ionic bond (ī on' ik) a type of bond in which ions are held together by the strong attraction of their opposite charges

ion (ī' on) a charged particle formed from an atom or atoms that have gained or lost one or more electrons

isotopes (ī' sə tōps') atoms of the same element with different numbers of neutrons

mass the amount of matter in an object

mass number the sum of protons and neutrons in an atom

mixture two or more elements or compounds that are blended without combining chemically

molecule (mol' ə kūl') neutral particle formed by atoms bonded chemically; may be an element or a compound

neutralization a process in which hydronium ions from an acid combine with hydroxide ions from a base to form water and a salt

neutralization reaction (nü' trə lə zā' shən) the reaction of an acid and a base to form a salt and water

nucleus (nû' klē əs) the central portion of an atom containing neutrons and protons

organic chemistry the study of carbon compounds

organic compound compound that contains carbon, and usually bonded to hydrogen, oxygen, or other non-metals

periodic table an arrangement of the chemical elements in rows according to increasing atomic numbers, in vertical columns having similar properties

periods the horizontal rows of the periodic table

physical changes changes in size, shape, color, or state; changes without a change in chemical composition

physical property a property or characteristic of a substance

polar molecules a molecule that is positively charged at one end and negatively charged at the other end

reactant (rē ak′ tənt) a substance that undergoes a chemical change

salt compound containing a positive ion from a base and a negative ion from an acid

solution (sə lü′ shən) a homogeneous mixture in which one substance (solute) is dissolved uniformly in another substance (solvent)

suspension (sə spen′ shən) heterogeneous mixture in which the particles are large enough to be seen; particles will eventually settle out

Tyndall effect colloid particles scattering a beam of light

volume the amount of space occupied by an object, measured in units of lengths cubed

INDEX

INDEX continued

CREDITS

Photo Credits:

Cover, The Image Bank/Michael Pasozior; **1,** Steven Fuller, Peter Arnold; **3,** (b) Chuck O'Rear/Westlight; (t) KS Studios; **5,** (br) Chuck O'Rear/Westlight; (bl) KS Studios; **8,** ©Doug Martin; **9,** Annie Griffiths/Westlight; **10,** (l) Yoav Levy/Phototake, (r) ©Studiohio; **11,** (l) Yoav Levy/Phototake; **13,** ©Steven Fuller/Peter Arnold, Inc.; **14,** ©KS Studios, /1991; **15,** Yoav Levy/Phototake; **16,** Grant Heilman; **17,** ©Brent Turner/BLT Productions/1991; **21,** N.V.R./Dave Williamson; **22,** ©Studiohio; **23,** Chuck O'Rear/Westlight; **24,** ©A.B.Joyce/Photo Researchers; **26, 27,** NASA; **28, 29,** ©Studiohio; **30,** Runk/Schoenberger/Grant Heilman Photography, Inc.; **30, 31,** ©Joseph Nettis/Photo Researchers; **31,** ©Brent Turner/BLT Productions/1991; **33,** Guy Motil/Westlight; **34,** Weyerhaeuser Paper Company, (m) Grant Heilman; **36,** ©John Sanford, Science Source/Photo Researchers; **37,** NASA; **38, 39,** ©Studiohio; **43,** ©David Scharf/Peter Arnold, Inc; **44,** ©Fermilab/Peter Arnold, Inc.; **46,** (tr) (br) Grant Heilman Photography, Inc., (ml) Barry L. Runk/Grant Heilman Photography, Inc.; (mr) ©Russ Lappa, Science Source/Photo Researchers, (bl); **47,** (tl) (mt) (bl) (bm) Runk/ Schoenberger/Grant Heilman Photography, Inc., (tm) (mb) Barry L. Runk/Grant Heilman Photography, Inc., (ml) (br) Grant Heilman Photography, Inc., (tr) ©Rich Treptow/Photo Researchers; **48, 49,** ©Studiohio; **50,** (l) Runk/ Schoenberger/Grant Heilman Photography, Inc., (m) (r) Barry L. Runk/Grant Heilman Photography, Inc.; **51,** (l) Earth Scenes/E.R. Degginger, (m) (r) Runk/Schoenberger/Grant Heilman Photography, Inc.; **58,** Chuck O'Rear/Westlight; **60, 61,** ©I.F.A./Peter Arnold, Inc.; **61,** ©Martin Coleman/Planet Earth Pictures; **62, 63,** ©Studiohio; **64,** (t) Richard Megna/Fundamental Photographs, (m) Color-Pic/E.R. Degginger; (b) Barry L. Runk/Grant Heilman Photography, Inc.; **69,** General Motors; **70,** (t) Barry L. Runk/Grant Heilman Photography, Inc., (b) ©KS Studios/1991; **71,** ©Jim Pickgagll/FPG International; **72,** NASA; **74, 75,** ©Doug Martin; **76, 77,** ©KS Studios/1991; **78,** S. Rannels/Grant Heilman Photography, Inc.; **79,** ©Brent Turner/BLT Productions/1991; **81,** Stuart Cohen, ©Comstock Inc., (b) AKZO Chemicals Inc.; **82,** ©Harvey Ldoyd/Peter Arnold, Inc.; **83,** (l) Richard Price/Westlight, (r) Bob Witkowski/Westlight; **84,** ©Martha Cooper/Peter Arnold, Inc.; **86, 87,** Larry Lefever/Grant Heilman Photography, Inc.; **88, 89,** ©KS Studios; **90,** (t) Cecile Brunswick/Peter Arnold, Inc. (m) ©Brent Turner/BLT Productions/1991; (b) ©Doug Martin; **91,** ©Brent Turner/BLT Productions/1991; **92,** Clyde H. Smith; **93,** Chuck O'Rear/Westlight; **94,** Michael Holford; **96, 97,** ©Dennis DiCicco/Peter Arnold, Inc.; **97,** (b) ©Dr. Mitsud Ohtsuki, Science Source/Photo Researchers; **98,** (tl) ©J&L Weber/Peter Arnold, Inc., (tr) ©John Cancalosi/Peter Arnold, Inc., (bl) ColorPic/Dr. E.R. Degginger, (br) ©Studiohio; **99,** NASA.

Illustration Credits:

6, Amanda Root; **7,** Irene Wareham; **18, 19, 20, 53,** Charlie Thomas; **32, 40, 41, 42, 64, 65, 66,** Henry Hill; **34,** Bill Boyer; **52, 54, 55, 57,** Thomas Kennedy; **67,** James Shough; **87,** Edward Coles; **99,** Ian Greathead